The Telegraph

CRYPTIC CROSSWORDS

8

An Hachette UK Company
www.hachette.co.uk

First published in Great Britain in 2020 by
Hamlyn, an imprint of Octopus Publishing Group Ltd,
Carmelite House, 50 Victoria Embankment, London EC4Y 0DZ
www.octopusbooks.co.uk

ISBN 978-0-600-63690-8

A CIP catalogue record for this book is available from the British Library.

Printed and bound in the UK

10 9 8 7 6 5 4 3 2

Telegraph Puzzles Editor: Chris Lancaster
Publishing Director: Trevor Davies
Creative Director: Jonathan Christie
Managing Editor: Sybella Stephens
Editor: Lesley Malkin
Editorial Assistant: Sarah Kyle
Page make-up: Dorchester Typesetting Group Ltd
Senior Production Manager: Peter Hunt
Production Controller: Serena Savini

The Telegraph

CRYPTIC CROSSWORDS 8

hamlyn

Editor's note

Welcome to the eighth book in our series of Cryptic Crosswords from the pages of *The Daily Telegraph*.

In 1925 *The Telegraph* was the first quality newspaper in the UK to publish a daily crossword, although those first puzzles looked quite different to the ones that you see today. Grids consisted of mainly white cells, and cryptic clues were in their infancy; one might find general knowledge clues, for instance, lurking among the anagrams and charades that one might find in today's cryptic crosswords. Within a few years, however, the crossword style that you see today was in place and has continued to this day.

In the intervening years much has changed in the world, but the *Telegraph* crossword has continued; the puzzles of today would not look out-of-place to solvers of those early crosswords. Clues have perhaps become somewhat more accessible over the years with less reliance on classical references and more on pop culture; technology has also moved on, and solvers are as likely to be tackling the crosswords on a mobile device or on the Telegraph Puzzles website as they are in the printed newspaper.

The compilers have also changed; there is a team of ten who set the *Telegraph* crossword, each of whom has their own style and trademarks which, after a while, are easily recognisable. For example, if you find a puzzle that contains a few religious references, it's probably the work of Don Manley, our regular Friday compiler; it's also a rare puzzle by Ray Terrell, one of our Thursday compilers, that doesn't include a clue that uses 'the Queen' to indicate ER.

Even though things have changed over the years, the basic ethos behind the *Telegraph* crossword is the same as it has always been: to provide a battle of wits between solver and compiler that's fair and enjoyable, and that is ultimately won by the solver. We hope the puzzles in this compendium will keep you entertained. Happy puzzling!

Chris Lancaster
Puzzles Editor

Puzzles

Across

1 Writing for a foreign film implied accepting sex (8)
5 To sing and dance about a 5-0 rout is heartless (6)
9 It's common sense there's a purpose in feeling sick (8)
10 Copper approaching end of tether with hardly any time to be indoors (6)
12 Insist a sure thing's sound (6)
13 A chick originally in nest — or older bird? (8)
15 Anorak from free catalogue? No thanks (7)
16 Monster on the retreat in *Mother Goose* (4)
20 Beyond its shelf life's no time to be selling (4)
21 Party leader's extremely snazzy, stylish and spiritual (7)
25 Applaud it or yawn inwardly — it's to do with what you hear (8)
26 Regretting using Parisian street that's almost completely jammed (6)
28 It's a '51 Citroen's front that's sloping (6)
29 Act out a search in burial place (8)
30 Suppose there's no power to carry on (6)
31 Ribbons go in weaving (8)

Down

1 What was afoot in *Cakes and Ale*? (6)
2 Surface discoloration may come from tea and coffee, it's said (6)
3 Sweet rice came cooked (3,5)
4 Celebrate tandem making a comeback (4)
6 Sharpness of article combined with extremes of emotion (6)
7 Kill hart and doe with clean shot away from the gaze of spectators (3-5)
8 Checked time Lawrence returned clutching fizzy water (8)
11 Change the ending of popular fellow's talks with second half cut (7)

1

14 Associate with Tory type (7)
17 To train fruit trees – cultivated pears – may take invention (8)
18 Happy student capers in party clothes (4,4)
19 Fire without heat ultimately is fake (8)
22 Central courtyard a partial success (6)
23 Spain and France keep striving (6)
24 One in suit – Burberry – outwardly sociable (6)
27 Information a bit topsy-turvy (4)

Across

1 One looking for clues left in houses? (6)
5 Funny play deficient, now sadly a disappointment (8)
9 Actor's headline portrayal of Saul's conversion (4,6)
10 Something on meal table in lounge (4)
11 Mum carrying antique through part of Europe (8)
12 State unfortunately having a king overthrown (6)
13 A female runs round for a hairdo (4)
15 Writer in South Africa having to hang around (8)
18 Elvis in huge theatre initially drowned by instrument (8)
19 Former tennis champ put on the scales, we hear (4)
21 University better than the others, one having a wonderful situation (6)
23 A maiden and friend hoarding gold with no concern for ethical values (8)
25 Small twins, first pair to get lost (4)
26 Church in which the French soldiers will be given money and fruit (10)
27 What may be found in school textbook, awful grey tome (8)
28 Old Greek graduate stuck within that time (6)

Down

2 Old volunteers work in region of South Island (5)
3 Clumsy matador, I will get twisted round bull's tail (9)
4 Put off the woman — darling not to have ring (6)
5 Come in to pal's, say, after accident, showing sympathy (15)
6 Finish with blame flying around -- not going to scrap yet? (8)
7 What Euclid saw as a triangle? (5)
8 Feeble report of Sunday-to-Saturday requirement (4-5)
14 Severe bodily condition — what could be best for it? (9)

16 City that may be built when the incoming waves have been destructive? (9)
17 Smart, having washed wound? (5-3)
20 Look towards the setting sun, being most depressed (6)
22 King and his son maybe half cut before noon (5)
24 Woman in peril, in danger (5)

The Telegraph

Across

1 Attractive romantic heroine about to be possessed (6)
4 Platform for small restaurant, some say, to get touted around (8)
9 Dig out food on table? (4,2)
10 Eagerly waiting for rum to pine to (2,6)
11 Unwell between the sheets yet supposed to be taking part (6)
12 Joy's plant, left by bishop (8)
14 Party politician may pen article spilling secrets (10)
18 High-flier's song which holds the opening to top places to see stars (10)
22 Clubman sounds revolutionary! (8)
23 Pretty self-contained — nice conversion (6)
24 Clock off and take care! (5,3)
25 Treacle endlessly refined to make booze (6)
26 Allowed to break silence before start of day (8)
27 Sneering single man's in charge (6)

Down

1 Songster that has been barred (4-4)
2 Right-o, sweetheart! (8)
3 Hearts up front — ordinary, needing to exploit crafty winger (8)
5 Agree periodic payment is coming together (10)
6 It comes between one landing and the next (6)
7 Yogurts carry evenly separated elements, causing complaint (6)
8 Bird following river in twittering host on air (6)
13 A time and place — rest will go round old city when one likes (2,8)
15 Fusspot left label outside (8)
16 Number of copies made from photograph on course (5,3)
17 Drug needed on Arctic manoeuvres (8)

3

19 Scoop: Rex to appear in something absorbing (6)
20 Stationary in street, meeting a jerk (6)
21 Waif's staggering, topless ... and bottomless (6)

8

Across

1 In fairness, breaking bail is a likelihood (11)
9 Watchful braves not seen around (9)
10 Poet takes orders (5)
11 Cavalryman turns back not thinking about us (6)
12 Takes in Uncle Sid when thrown out (8)
13 Try, to prevent a try? (6)
15 Not so anxious since replacement's arrived? (8)
18 A blooming avalanche! (8)
19 Supplies rushed on board (6)
21 Certainly a variety of tuberose (2,2,4)
23 Box Popeye, maybe, with nothing held back (6)
26 Strangely eager to come to terms (5)
27 Honour Seb Coe in a sculpting (9)
28 Give a Royal Marine's guard order to salute (7,4)

Down

1 He foresees support before the reforms (7)
2 Well-equipped place for caravans en route (5)
3 Sent flying! (9)
4 Scottish boy about five who had a terrible reputation (4)
5 Fiancee at home and cared for (8)
6 Countryman of fifty under servitude (5)
7 Brooded about one's being exploited (7)
8 Transfer worker superfluous to requirements (8)
14 They give lift when a flier goes over obstacles (8)
16 It's neither here nor there (2,7)
17 Game for two couples, but involving more of us (8)
18 Stuff and eat as it is cooked (7)
20 Boy with nets and lines (7)
22 Headlong plunge into water (5)
24 Singer put right after wrong note (5)
25 Piece of ice destined to give way (4)

4

Across

1 Man very curious about slogan sung in fleet (8,4)
8 Animal watering hole in which smell's appalling at first (7)
9 Liner hit it, an iceberg somewhat hidden (7)
11 Husbandry up to the time of elderliness (7)
12 Saw king finished in lead (7)
13 Hit back about law (5)
14 Hindu text discovered in ark, a must for translation by head of academy (4,5)
16 Advance payments required to secure audio player? The direct opposite (9)
19 Man's lost Wings hit of long ago? (5)
21 Theft: criminal nearly caught inside (7)
23 Claptrap from detective was hard to follow (7)
24 Helena's here in Piedmont, a native (7)
25 Trendy type touring hospital, briefly (2,5)
26 Pitching on new lawn (7,5)

Down

1 Singer, a Jackson, in pop band in Mali, performing (7)
2 Batter and break bulwark (7)
3 Browbeaten ambassador knight kissed quickly (9)
4 Don overturned tennis call (3,2)
5 Ideas on it son scuppered (7)
6 Price e.g. of outlet incorporated therein (7)
7 Station in London being supplied with choice fruit (8,4)
10 Excitedly watch bee and a big butterfly (7-5)
15 Overcoming it, Germans reassembled (9)
17 Wrong about working round place in Ontario (7)
18 Overcome dire peril crossing Virginia (7)
19 Direct extra to spot (7)
20 Cavalryman, a stupid person to support Democrat as well as Republican (7)
22 Long story about Spain (5)

5

5

Across

1 Basic assumption of stance against drink? (11)
10 Feeling sorry about judge's determination to free student (5)
11 'Relate' organised paper with volunteers at home (9)
12 Manual controls on top of fairground attractions? (9)
13 Join by just accepting the end of bombing (5)
14 Convincing information for son in price (6)
16 Reluctant to get a makeover without length cut short (8)
18 Fruitful but diminutive academic, around fifty-one, in charge (8)
20 First pair of horses in front of home straight (6)
23 Devices for picking up new clothes outside (5)
24 Where to see judge giving space to romance? (9)
26 Old maid, for example, wrapping book and exercising vigilance (9)
27 Power of jet fighter leads to high tension (5)
28 Forecast covering area workers creates a sticky situation (11)

Down

2 Make one from backing asset in university (5)
3 Heavy metal bars putting pressure on unusual origin (3,4)
4 Dubious environment for new drink (6)
5 Hanging records go! (8)
6 Fork out a ransom for one in eight (7)
7 Concentration before calling (13)
8 Bearing the cost of conveyance (8)
9 Assign a low value to muted trainees in disarray (13)
15 Personal quality of Eros, say, full of love and endless sense (for a change) (8)
17 Cut back on tough fish (8)
19 Financial institution that's fashionable, of course, on river (7)

6

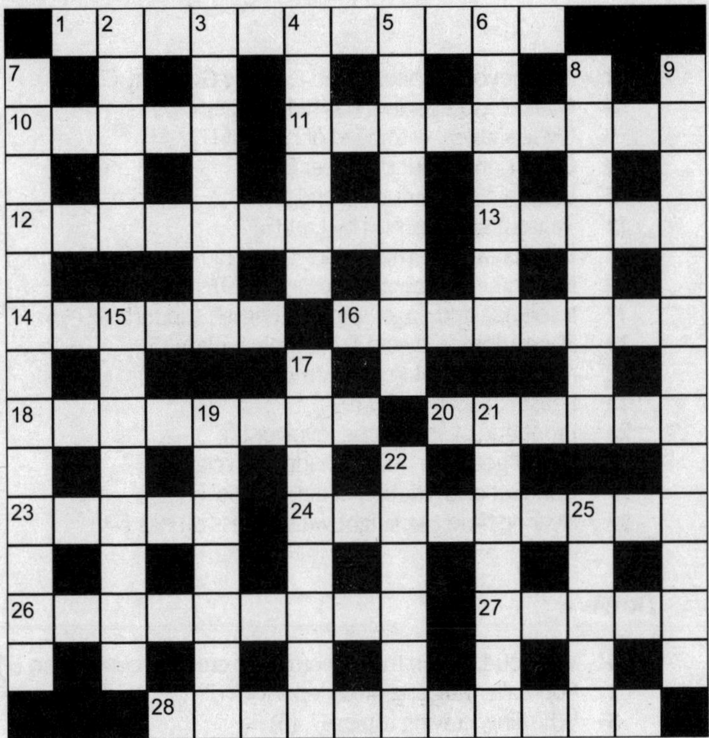

21 Choose single parent as best (7)
22 Unsophisticated game with set, since losing regulars (6)
25 Producer of music newspaper, for example (5)

6

Across

1 Taught you French, pulled apart by Germany (7)
5 Grant Bono's partner has hidden talent (7)
9 Close shaven, with head of hair cut (7)
10 Good sign producing cheer (7)
11 Lady in far off fantasy world (9)
12 Peasant's oppression by Left (5)
13 Baby creature almost alongside timid creature (5)
15 Battery's run-down in motorway (9)
17 Insolence and anger gripping English supporter (9)
19 Shoe adopted by old Toulousain initially (5)
22 Aroused all right in amazement (5)
23 Feast is, I'd fancy, full (9)
25 Front end of snub nose revolver (7)
26 Out of gear, the nude's made from clay (7)
27 Conduct examination of girl's school (7)
28 Nearing time, duck fight with gutless drunks (7)

Down

1 Very loud, one in truck overturned creating congestion (7)
2 Footballer hugging provided shock (7)
3 Whistling, craving topless… (5)
4 …ride, and gasp uncontrollably taking a knock (9)
5 Conservative leader past it? Shut up! (5)
6 Lily, after a daft hit, flipped (9)
7 Take a leak outside with flash (7)
8 Could be Queen's payment for performance (7)
14 Get out of sun's heat, heading inside (9)
16 Arranged matter over hospital department's handling (9)
17 Bass weighed and cooked (7)
18 Endlessly stimulate following a second of love (7)
20 More careless loose talk? (7)
21 News, it's old, racket with gang's head captured (7)
23 Row around river to find fish (5)

7

24 The woman's about right, women nag (5)

Across

1 Lively person's lapse into sin involving anger against bishop (8)
5 Encourage doctor having trouble in city (6)
9 German graduate different, wasting time (8)
10 Clergy flats in which you'll get lessons on Bible etc? (6)
12 American gangster uses deceit to get supporters (6)
13 In the course of a day crew becomes oppressed (8)
15 Nervous? Extremely after answer given to question (7)
16 'Oven-like' about covers what it is (4)
20 Protection for old soldier, Irishman retreating (4)
21 Son has heart, a persistent type (7)
25 Desire to get on? No, I'm a bit sloppy! (8)
26 Made a big effort with oven, having grabbed recipe initially (6)
28 Very good in performance as traveller Dick (6)
29 Publication that may be packed with explosive material (8)
30 Scraper of muck from verge by turning of road (6)
31 Nude mostly covered in mud? Not a recommended medical treatment! (5-3)

Down

1 Socialist prejudice all but admitted by enthusiast (6)
2 Criticise former England football manager crossing line (6)
3 A rude drunk carries around container for wine (8)
4 Almost memorise nonsense this man wrote (4)
6 Fruit gives ape energy (6)
7 Retreat from strange ritual based around part of Bible (4,4)
8 What tenant pays to hold party in dwelling (8)
11 One's for hauling up Richard, blunder having been admitted (7)
14 Old vessel one gets on, cheering (7)
17 This writer's to be given role, paper's boss communicated (8)

18 Near orb I melted, like Icarus? (8)
19 Being artistic, chucked in a money-oriented job (4-4)
22 Good person to lasso a number of horses? (6)
23 One's probably spotted maiden in love after party (6)
24 Church has authentic stuff for harvest festival? (6)
27 Religious adherent is a plain girl from what we hear? (4)

Across

4 By end of over I had ball causing dismissal (8)
8 Dolly has heart turned by regular customer (6)
9 Area of beauty can produce moist eye (8)
10 Church built initially with a quartz material (8)
11 Suffering two low grades in examination (6)
12 Foreign noblewoman to defraud savings account once (8)
13 Is annoying society without cause (8)
16 Shrub, being at home in desert, to become sickly when uprooted (8)
19 Devil gets handle on familiar address (8)
21 Beat Obama, for example, one after another (6)
23 When school is open football team's back to get together (8)
24 Cheat friend holding in to keep under control (8)
25 Secure after breakout and free from danger (6)
26 Control opening to create in new form (8)

Down

1 Quiet region of Spain, one that's just perfect (7)
2 Truce after weapon destroyed cities (9)
3 Unmentionable things zombie does? (6)
4 Three men get coin to go round one famous golf course (5,3,7)
5 Find record finished (8)
6 Did 'urt with weapons (5)
7 Blade snubbed girl (7)
14 She cleans Californian city strip (9)
15 American beach barbecue where Madeleine perhaps eats meat (8)
17 Sailor with no company gets seafood (7)
18 Rascal with debts spurning religion (7)
20 Provides West End show entertaining Her Majesty (6)
22 Condescend to exclude son from plan (5)

9

Across

1 One's likely to budget for inexpensive fish (10)
9 Hash settled for Middle Eastern ruler (4)
10 Neat electrical network that keeps farm animals in a field (6,4)
11 Architectural style about right? That's sarcastic! (6)
12 Not birds, but they chirp and fly (7)
15 Traveller allowed key is satisfied (7)
16 Bags of patients (5)
17 Champions of the pack (4)
18 Pay attention or bend over (4)
19 Starts the game off with defeats (5)
21 Arrests for minor assaults? (7)
22 He fleeces his clients (7)
24 After a drive, one walks (6)
27 One holds hands during the game (4,6)
28 Growth of love at first sight (4)
29 Metal shackles — they keep men in step (5,5)

Down

2 It precedes the final passion (4)
3 Cause of breathing difficulty found? Hats off to mother! (6)
4 The woman has to ring up for varnish (7)
5 Foreign port area (4)
6 Tips that I've cut for salad (7)
7 Hire candle out, giving superior illumination (10)
8 Smart girl seen in a city (10)
12 Flying saucer? (4,6)
13 Chars at night to get debt written off (5,5)
14 Where we can buy with money off drink on board (5)
15 Splits payments for accommodation (5)
19 What this youngster's mother did? (4,3)
20 Phrases articulated by Himalayans (7)
23 A capital rank Arab holds (6)

10

25 Time to come up before a court (4)
26 Electric wire to act as a conductor (4)

Across

1 Old American who takes pledge? (6)
4 Original child likely to be favourite (4-2)
8 Turn crimson about unknown Old Boy network (8)
10 Hot, unwholesome stifling temperature (6)
11 Basic loyalties covering up disgust (4)
12 To resign in questionable circumstances ignoring leader is common (10)
13 Wanton petulance involving a caught and bowled is not to be tolerated (12)
16 Undecided when trick is seen in full (12)
20 Disregard northern cold in nightie (10)
21 Roll up in coat that gets left behind (4)
22 Cold plain fish doctor's eaten (6)
23 It's heavenly in this place and others around (8)
24 Sharp bend in track before part of course (6)
25 Feature with old records reviewed in turn (6)

Down

1 Norm twisted ankle here in Mayfair (4,4)
2 Out-of-tune backing in *God Only Knows* (5)
3 Gourmet wants large-scale curries now and then (7)
5 Following start of divorce violent brutish husband wanting to cause upset (7)
6 Wild West scenes exuding cold charm (9)
7 Denim bush jackets a sign of bad weather? (6)
9 Principal canteen in a mess for repairs (11)
14 American fast food? Cool, I will get chow maybe (6,3)
15 In the past actors could be leaden (8)
17 Relative got acne badly (7)
18 Guerrilla leader surrounded by dregs and hangers-on (7)
19 Put money into protecting European Community? That'll be fruitful! (6)
21 Conifers recorded in gorse (5)

11

11

Across

1 Criticism levelled as result of trophies recently stolen (3,4)
5 Embarrasses a party before elections, losing heart (7)
9 Month here without walls is a bore! (5)
10 Pub's motto, possibly? (7,2)
11 Manage to hear what's said for slogans? (10)
12 Platform that is accepted by proportional representation (4)
14 Cover pan with half of tomato, for a simple dish (6,6)
18 Fear arrest (12)
21 Team returns eating live goat! (4)
22 Arrangement for piano and sitar? Some hope (10)
25 Tested by a Parisian, without any restraints (9)
26 Picture periodical found in empty institute (5)
27 Causes irritation, but agrees with name for first of sons (7)
28 Suspect increase lacks answer, being honest (7)

Down

1 Fish's source of iron in situ? (6)
2 Merry wives finally getting something to cover legs (6)
3 Hurried to welcome daughter and boss, being shrewd (4-6)
4 Forbidden fruit – finally getting a raspberry! (5)
5 Remedies for workers having to die horribly inside (9)
6 Out of control in the morning, then fine (4)
7 Hot Lips worked outside area infirmary (8)
8 Rigour oddly absent under great boss (8)
13 Ceremony, for my people embracing love (10)
15 Retain bets, with no time for tokens (9)
16 Act strangely on island, and go quiet (8)
17 Reduce support for part of Oxford, perhaps – that's a blow (8)
19 Conclusion when penalty crosses a line (6)
20 A former girlfriend on the phone from the extension (6)

23 Try leaving business in Asian river delta (5)
24 Live without diamonds, comfortably (4)

Across

7 Key impression made around motorway north (7)
8 Old Chancellor with very regal character at all events (7)
10 Uncertain situation for a high-flier? (2,2,3,3)
11 Drop reportedly in rank (4)
12 Only nameless lad is sadly lacking faith (8)
14 A dope clearly disheartened in business (6)
15 Property magazine giving one chance to be with loved ones? (7,4)
19 Beam and bloody equipment having to be put back (6)
20 Criminal is a sort to possess naphtha initially (8)
22 Student gripped by selfishness retracted amorous glance (4)
23 Fair woman getting measure of horse in end possibly (4-6)
25 Mental image of fellow worker when by yard (7)
26 Lower figure in field getting plant (7)

Down

1 Part of castle appropriate for exercises (4,3)
2 European mentioned part of fish (4)
3 Walk ostentatiously for instance around tree (6)
4 Exotic root included in previous times in dish (3,5)
5 Fish, perhaps? Then raw meat cooked with time running out (10)
6 Backs element in legal case (7)
9 On which a cross may be exhibited for those standing? (6,5)
13 High street concern as a French doctor with little energy tucked into coffee (10)
16 Beer glass manufactured with no end of aplomb making substantial gift? (8)
17 Indian tourist site appears in dull plan (7)
18 Austere figure from church stopping wine clubs (7)
21 Train group of swimmers? (6)

13

24 Set of tables featuring in fine store (4)

13

Across

8 The male artist presenting goddess (4)
9 Consume beef maybe (not starter though) (3)
10 Virtually noon? A long time before that (6)
11 Beware of sailors en masse in old Liverpool club! (6)
12 An editor being awkward should be limited (8)
13 New starship – it's cosy for scientists studying heavenly bodies (15)
15 Kitchen item not working with its required temperature not quite attained? (7)
17 Silver Circle like a cruise ship going nowhere fast! (7)
20 Sad spinster's art weirdly representing symbols of a nation (5,3,7)
23 Supplier offers endless words of wisdom, concealing identity (8)
25 As a pupil 'tensed up' according to report (6)
26 'Alpine' could be clued as 'from a mountainous land' (6)
27 The whole amount? Sounds to be less than that (3)
28 Channel Four's last item – brilliant! (4)

Down

1 Trees that could be seen as sacred (6)
2 Start to criticise a judge missing core point being happy-go-lucky (8)
3 Have one last exotic trip, using various seaplanes indeed (3,6,3,3)
4 Floors in shops containing the latest thing for everybody (7)
5 The men suffering with agitation making demand for measured progress (3,5,2,1,4)
6 Work involving short performance with one famous actor (6)
7 Expelled reportedly for being indecent (4)
14 Brown relish not good (3)

16 Drivel from flipping historian (3)
18 Writing about life after death (8)
19 Location for speech (7)
21 Go on a spree that includes a show (6)
22 English Conservative taken in by this set of values (6)
24 Falter as revolutionary losing heart (4)

14

Across

1 Foremost of ladies always will take time to make purchase (8)
5 Hangover from the freeze (6)
9 Thin mist obscured metalworker (8)
10 New Testament taken from monastic rambling of Biblical character? (6)
11 Try to include the whole vegetable (7)
12 Basil with group outside, getting fizzy drink (7)
13 One's not conscious of his progress (11)
16 Vehicle taking wife and cad to Cumbrian town (11)
21 Bird enthusiast wants dog (7)
22 Double misfortune, receiving Western hostility (3-4)
23 Collapse caused by calcium meeting artery? (4,2)
24 Emergency measures to make tree steady (5,3)
25 Signed idiotic plan (6)
26 Shopkeeper disinclined to get in ground rice (8)

Down

1 News of the French sports fixture (6)
2 Val literally a hooligan! (6)
3 Capital's co-founder rebuilt our slum (7)
4 Fail to visit one of the fortifications (2,2,3,4)
6 Disease is caught – cut short holiday time (7)
7 Make a hash of meal back in US picnic (8)
8 Alien comes to create upset and so on (8)
12 Splendid to be seen with Parisian here in Cornish river, on the surface (11)
14 Insincere pair confronted (3-5)
15 Man on top of island's mountain (3,5)
17 Letting outspoken general make notes (7)
18 Firmly established source on film location (4-3)
19 Kay and I with Gail travelling from African city (6)
20 Grand being on top, and on Queen's aircraft (6)

15

15

Across

1 A married woman in the country (7)
5 Gives the call-sign (7)
9 Funny to see a number walk like sailors (5)
10 Today's most popular writer? (9)
11 Legal compulsion to be a suitor? (5,5)
12 Travel authority needed as one's in Virginia (4)
14 Well-known bowler in scarf, perhaps, gets a duck (7,5)
18 Strange thing, gin and bitters, for celebrated singers (12)
21 Women's Aid initially provided for homeless child (4)
22 Amazed as mum refused to work (10)
25 There's not much to say for having it (9)
26 Wines blended for strength (5)
27 Spouse to join a bridge player (7)
28 Itinerant craftsman? (7)

Down

1 One habitually taking things did wrong in law (6)
2 Big racial issue? (6)
3 I will repeat: 'That's ignorant!' (10)
4 A shade of caution (5)
5 One hoping to become a winner on points (9)
6 Headland under which one may shelter (4)
7 First love in a girl is moving (8)
8 Feeling fed-up? (8)
13 He pays the price of publicity (10)
15 Haricot bean, for example, not for a starter (3-6)
16 Second doctor takes in present to work – a plant (8)
17 Silver on recent issue, sparkling (8)
19 Give up and go to bed (4,2)
20 Joint holder (6)
23 Fish seems to be right in the light (5)
24 Examination of what verse should do? (4)

16

1		2		3		4	■	5		6		7		8
	■		■		■		■		■		■		■	
9					■	10								
	■		■		■		■		■		■		■	
11										■	12			
	■		■		■	■	■		■	13	■		■	
■	■	■	14			15								
16	■	17	■		■		■		■		■		■	
18												■	■	■
	■		■		■		■	■	■		■	19	■	20
21				■	22			23						
	■		■	24	■		■		■		■		■	
25									■	26				
	■		■		■		■		■		■		■	
27							■	28						

Across

1 Turn down quantity of Chinese food (3,3)
5 Save? Sailor has a method (4,4)
9 Vagrant knocked unconscious? (4-3-3)
10 Male, hostile in factory (4)
11 Sense agreement amongst rowing crew (8)
12 Shrewd showing sculpted statue (6)
13 Pretty fine tune (4)
15 Diet, terrible at first for army unit (8)
18 Left, sadly, with external injury — a break (4-4)
19 Fix dish of food (4)
21 Think highly of other side having dropped foremost of strikers (6)
23 Lip in instruments that are blown to make glasses (4-4)
25 Cut rolls sent back (4)
26 Like staff serving drinks inside? (6,4)
27 Spring flower, one seen in fall at Aspen? (8)
28 Level, holding the Parisian football team (6)

Down

2 Film director in trailer entered by soldiers (5)
3 Secretary's initial answer's to get rid of raised typeface (4,5)
4 Train myself to straddle a horse (6)
5 Speak bluntly, as gunslingers used to do? (5,4,3,3)
6 Greatly disturbed about hospital's apathetic state (8)
7 Acknowledge a senior policeman has seized millions over time (5)
8 Suddenly everyone's in agreement about leader of council (3,2,4)
14 Legendary king soon bagged prey on top of mountain (9)
16 Contemptible money-grubber's up to it (9)
17 Be sure about subscriber (8)
20 Fruit in orchard's first row (6)

17

1	2		3		4	■	5		6		7		8	

22 Joint, minutes from Tobermory, perhaps, heading north (5)
24 Inspector getting extra drop of Scotch in (5)

17

Across

1 Biscuits and scrambled eggs in turn (6,4)
6 Dessert's no good (4)
10 Fish is no good in beer (5)
11 Bribe a substitute? (9)
12 Winner has one in front of a queen (8)
13 The best swot welcomes start of exams (5)
15 Licence charge about right — act married! (7)
17 People who can absorb information are parasites (7)
19 Goes to a restaurant in castle at Southport (4,3)
21 Biscuit from Madeira, say, on vessel with clipped prow (7)
22 Misses sleep on board ship (5)
24 Quietly cut down by soldiers, having got ready (8)
27 Place trap to upset this! (5-4)
28 Cut around the base of horn and grind (5)
29 Put back smooth tailless fish (4)
30 Hamlet, for example, gets mainly faithful worker to skive (4,6)

Down

1 Animal from Indian state east of Gujarat (4)
2 Careless in short nightdress — not without love (9)
3 Authority with no power to wield (5)
4 Lad getting up on time with strange remedy (7)
5 Flipping good service in the best digital coverage (7)
7 Heartily pull and eat leg bones (5)
8 The arsonist's foe ties farmer in knots (4-6)
9 Continue to resist project (5,3)
14 Pudding? Own cheeky alcoholic preparation (10)
16 Act on gold measure threshold (8)
18 A distraught mate held in unfinished prison camp in part of America (9)
20 Betters suffer trapped wind here on board! (7)

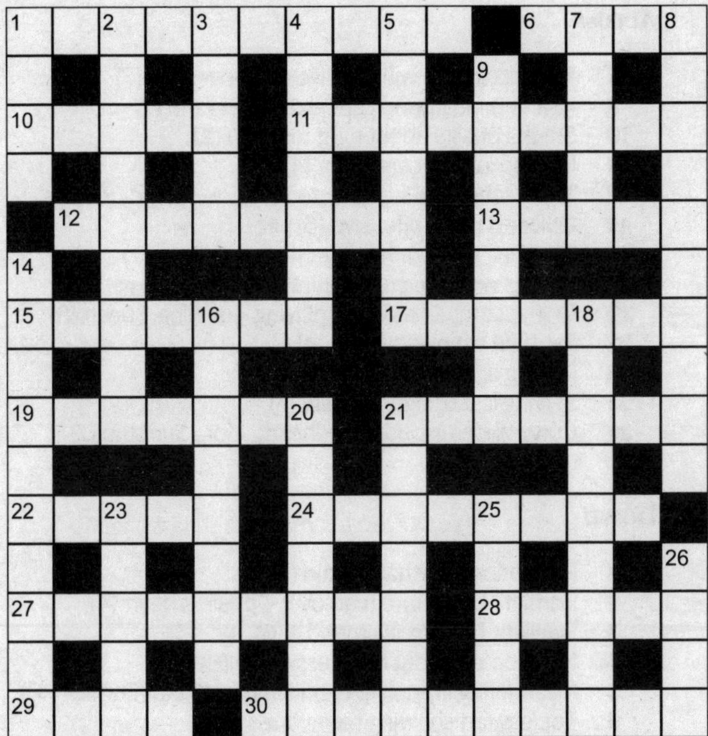

21 Brazenly finished those without stockings — lady gets disheartened (7)

23 Drive leaves member in poor lie (5)

25 Irritation comes from linking of exchange rates (5)

26 Bill's child (4)

Across

7 Terrorist leader with motive for subversion (7)
8 Insane time around capital of Ibiza island (7)
10 Stock's quality about right for soup (10)
11 Married in rush ceremony (4)
12 'Unattached' girl's connected to Greek island (8)
14 Officer is more offensive (6)
15 'Number Ten' ace has it worked out (11)
19 Bristles when given Indian state support (6)
20 One accompanies bloke playing, covering Queen (8)
22 Satisfied eating ace food (4)
23 Making a pittance, I expect (10)
25 Serving last of lager in brew (7)
26 Curvy nudes including redhead before *Sun* strip (7)

Down

1 Promotion puff that is plain (7)
2 Hamlet? Desperate man over Ophelia's heart (4)
3 Swelling, blood goes round it (6)
4 Not worried about heartless judge (8)
5 Meandering French river bridging 'rue'? Not English! (10)
6 Topless tart showing some brass (7)
9 Tame Scottie made to perform (11)
13 Form of criminal's bird done before time ends (10)
16 Twist a lever to lift (8)
17 Fashion do turns into monotony (7)
18 Hardy woman supporting house guests finally? (7)
21 A thrill taking Charlie to get higher (6)
24 Bit role (4)

19

19

Across

9 Smell coming from party in old, old city (5)
10 Capital city to suffer loss of life when captured by British officer (9)
11 Worker protected in secure American city (5,2)
12 Like fans making fuss meeting group (7)
13 Greek detectives about to apprehend men (5)
14 Gloomy nature with sin needing to be put right (9)
16 Provides variety – it's what one who knows the ropes does (5,3,7)
19 Donkey left in very good pasture (9)
21 I had taken the initiative and watched others working? (5)
23 Cloud with one edge changing, appearing as a mound (7)
25 A report shocking magistrate once (7)
27 Perfume that's special to wearers (9)
28 Discover knight sitting by river beyond meadow (5)

Down

1 Manage to cry when upset over son not getting on (4)
2 One who signs up as member of carpenter's team? (6)
3 Fat groups of actors in TV shows? (10)
4 What makes bishop be taken in by idiot woman trying to be religious? (6)
5 Part of splendid act I contrived teaching (8)
6 The old man with nothing may be seen going round room (4)
7 Little woman in aquatic sport falling apart (8)
8 Horrible woman clothed in soft colour advanced (10)
13 Insulting rogue without hesitation, a member of Government? (10)
15 Abseiler to wobble holding a line? It's within the bounds of possibility (10)
17 Like teacher's pet in mishap that's almost disastrous (4,4)
18 They may help you to hear top groups (8)

20

20 Quit indoor sport shortly after grabbing record (6)
22 All the worse for being vicious (6)
24 The French world, first and last, is vulgar (4)
26 Money must be managed with diligence initially (4)

Across

1 Yearning after net returns may be seductive (10)
6 Man hugging wife was dizzy (4)
9 Fish behind second rock (5)
10 No rises unfortunately around European Community – in this? (9)
12 Crazy sect is looting member of church (13)
14 'Elpful suggestion stopped fiancé (8)
15 An old hand, one putting on a show (6)
17 See bistro house red primarily and a container for it (6)
19 Is copper being entertained by Scottish football club making a bloomer? (8)
21 The antibodies destroyed illicit lover (1,3,2,3,4)
24 Devious Roman made notes (9)
25 I spot one to be taken in – him? (5)
26 Maybe use O2 arena (4)
27 Western character to cringe in fear receiving blow (10)

Down

1 Money's not right for singer (4)
2 Something or other employing old serving women in religious festival (7)
3 In circuit, that man has to finish broadcasting detective story (3,4,2,4)
4 Dashing to look at unfinished area of North London (8)
5 May gets upset by endless hot Mexican food (5)
7 Overlooking one engaged in curling (7)
8 Economic theorist ruined minor state (10)
11 Insufficient vote for simple mathematical procedure (5,8)
13 Medic rails about refusal to take responsibility (10)
16 Mining hazard got rid of a politician (8)
18 Transport worker runs over wild animal (7)
20 Teacher is hoping to embrace nurse (7)
22 Relish old dance (5)

21

23 Create agitation in prison (4)

Across

1 Near-cold liquid that's found in the kitchen (8)
6 One is often cast as a tug-of-war team member (6)
9 Contemptible cheat goes back on promises to pay (6)
10 One running out of clothes (8)
11 Relaxed, with lowered pulse (8)
12 Attractive yacht at sea beyond Cape (6)
13 The Bench? (4,2,6)
16 It has the military stamp on it (6,6)
19 The sad gathering for bereavements (6)
21 He joins more than one union illegally (8)
23 *1984*? (8)
24 A ship's company overheard making hoard (6)
25 How often models losing shape may be employed? (6)
26 Fed pig inside — refused to acknowledge it (8)

Down

2 Familiar mode of address for ex-pupil? (3,3)
3 A party with sailors below deck (5)
4 Change of speed leads to speed which is reckless (9)
5 Its root goes into stew (7)
6 Maurice's heart of gold (5)
7 Many raced, getting beaten? (9)
8 Pass an examination (8)
13 Mum, badly treated, is devastated (9)
14 Sort of figure that changes with time? (4-5)
15 Like this place? Me too! (4,4)
17 Censured about plot involving UK (7)
18 Sculpted statue, showing ingenuity (6)
20 Bad weather in August or March (5)
22 Parrot with head of myna and a cry of a rook (5)

22

Across

1 Penelope in *Some Like It Hot*? (5)
4 Claimant's ugly pet (9)
9 At home with dishonest office-holder (9)
10 Good German car? Spanish designer! (5)
11 Where sleeper may find overnight accommodation (7)
12 In retirement boxer is the opposite of romantic (7)
13 Wet blanket getting soggier (6)
15 Magnificent woods run wild (8)
18 Ready for expedition Livingstone finally cracked (8)
20 Whispering walls of château? (6)
23 Support overwhelming single trailblazer (7)
24 Giant in fairy story (7)
26 Broadcast influenced kid (5)
27 Concept records for dreamers (9)
28 Femme fatale needs time before perm sets in new style (9)
29 Fear entry to dean's study (5)

Down

1 Anchor retaining unusually fine balance (5,4)
2 Drain curaçao bottles to suffer (5)
3 Stock ingredient of Rambo – hard rather than right, and outwardly naive (3,4)
4 Favour for each grasping judge (6)
5 Where waiter might be found? (8)
6 One who's close but pullin' back (7)
7 Union firm about wearing khaki or similar (2,7)
8 Fellow is not commonly liable to lose consciousness (5)
14 Gloomy place a wretched louse is held in silence (9)
16 Lost for words with dire Spurs thrashed (9)
17 Air needs to be recycled where passenger sits (8)
19 Excuse message before starting (7)
21 Squeaky clean? (7)

23

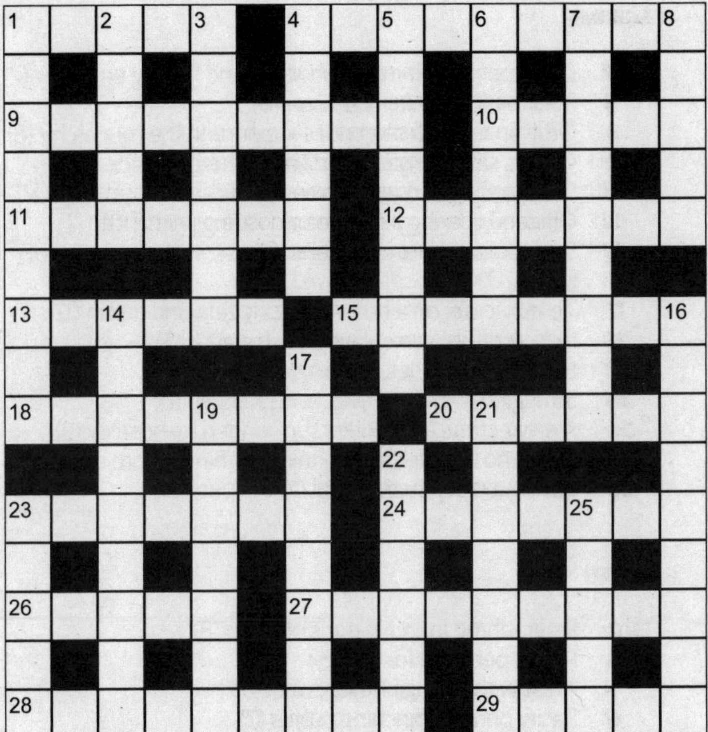

22 Cute plainclothes officer in country attire (6)
23 Job to admit one put forward (5)
25 No longer fashionable to scrape through finals with poor grade (5)

Across

1 Liverpool, for example, on strike and finding empathy (7)
5 Rock band opening a season (6)
9 Orbison and top celebrities supporting the monarchy (8)
11 Crown, say, finally reacted with wounded pride (6)
12 Disregarding dangers of skin infection (4)
13 Officers ordering a ride aboard sailing ships (10)
14 Such politicians are proper moaners, with no source of help (5-7)
17 Terribly cute, on a bus, American gets under skin (12)
21 Not on drugs, son delayed fresh start (5,5)
22 Laugh out loud, left in lounge (4)
23 Struggled to cross a river, and changed (6)
24 A great crime for soldiers surrounded by hostility (8)
25 One who believes in beginning to think before robbery (6)
26 Loving a party, make a call (7)

Down

2 Fragrant rug found in ruins of Cairo (8)
3 Pence per head for fruit (5)
4 Artist with Popular Front colours (7)
6 Pacify primate pinching pulses (7)
7 Agree bill and become silent (9)
8 Assumption drawn from article on Circle line (6)
10 How one may work out position of nomadic unit at large (11)
15 Allergic production has, in time, shifted (9)
16 Chamber, when full, has this report (8)
18 Live with teams, to boot (7)
19 Robot needing energy for day without using liquid (7)
20 Flexible growth must include one (6)
22 Primate involved in wholesale murder (5)

24

24

Across

1 Bug rat planted in American agency (6)
5 Struck and played gripping top of five iron (8)
9 'Offspring' providing accompaniment around finale (10)
10 Faint, losing head, showing fever (4)
11 A place, incredibly loaded, filled with gold (8)
12 Girl's fib about backside (6)
13 Bone usually located near adductor initially (4)
15 Sprinter valiantly bridging gap (8)
18 Comes into the house? (8)
19 Top primate approaches cross (4)
21 Dream when tart embraces redhead (6)
23 Whole of Queen brought back into being (8)
25 Chick's tender holding Romeo (4)
26 Fat reduction (10)
27 Imprisoned grass admits bloke died (8)
28 Ruddy woman's covered in blubber! (6)

Down

2 International trade standard (5)
3 Branch or agency includes foreign city (9)
4 Queen with Henry without hot temper (6)
5 A drug can tailor bodies' changes (8,7)
6 Heavyweight boxer typically ends in loss (8)
7 Guys in leather pants displaying rear (5)
8 Explain dodgy clue one time (9)
14 Left in saddle, breaking runaway (9)
16 Change order and put back on stove (9)
17 Went west round oceans becoming sick (8)
20 Constant interference? (6)
22 Donations raised supporting popular country (5)
24 Singer's time with right single in comeback (5)

25

1	2		3		4		5		6		7		8	
9											10			
11									12					
13	14						15				16			
					17									
18											19			
									20					
21			22				23						24	
25					26									
27									28					

Across

4 Tory literature produced by agreement (8)
8 Explosive young reporter confronting a queen (6)
9 Clegg gaining reputation – or Cleggy as that might be? (8)
10 Like many an entrepreneur, feels terribly keen to get stuck in (4-4)
11 Season in which Bury will need width at the start (6)
12 View offered by girl interrupting parents (8)
13 A group of violent ravers, exceptionally cross (8)
16 Agreeable Conservative hurrying to embrace maiden (8)
19 One may account for current restriction (8)
21 A convenience for people doing business (6)
23 Old PM's forebear not half making a packet? Certainly not! (8)
24 Nonsense about actress Diana being smug (8)
25 Stimulate love in an act of deception (6)
26 Artist's kettle? (8)

Down

1 Observe girl going round northern country (7)
2 Something bright and beautiful in tabloid – female sitting on cow! (9)
3 British granny eating a fruit (6)
4 One taking pictures gets rioter cavorting with champagne (15)
5 Habits of those who are buttoned up? (8)
6 Dispute at home after trip in car? (3-2)
7 Holidaymakers needing celebratory drink – husband goes out (7)
14 Why does a dame ultimately look different? It's the cosmetic (9)
15 Refuse to go into a filthy place? (8)
17 House with good paintings? Here's original artist (7)
18 Short introduction to crosswords is found in Chapter 1 (7)

20 Revolutionary regions needing the installation of a governor (6)

22 Drink and dope upset you and me (5)

Across

1 Cavalryman drops round, smart – one's all aflutter (9)
9 Movement provides topic for debate (6)
10 Master of strategy showing diplomacy in charge of Scotsman (9)
11 Drawing second boat (6)
12 Some hated building this house (9)
13 Was successful with left-wing backing, it's a miracle (6)
17 Form of worship (3)
19 Jester's desire – amusement sparked by a sentence? (8,2,5)
20 Skill seen in party piece (3)
21 Ring the woman in strife (6)
25 Risk these days putting outlet by river (9)
26 Creatively, I tarry – that's not common (6)
27 One's in one country or another (9)
28 Cricket side getting part of the wicket out temporarily? (2,4)
29 Gambler tours Bath perhaps to dish the dirt? (9)

Down

2 Sanity found in *About a Boy*? (6)
3 Collect two articles in Greece (6)
4 Tiny reforms accommodating this Parisian's subtle point (6)
5 Conduct the conga and cause mischief? (4,1,5,5)
6 Male fish or insect (9)
7 Active Fifties teenager's gone to get equipped (6,3)
8 Hermit as a result of her action, sadly (9)
14 Fellow's let down over drug in plant container (9)
15 Sign up to be an underwriter? (9)
16 Head of clan requires cook to admit one before volunteers get in (9)
17 Most of the fruit or vegetable (3)

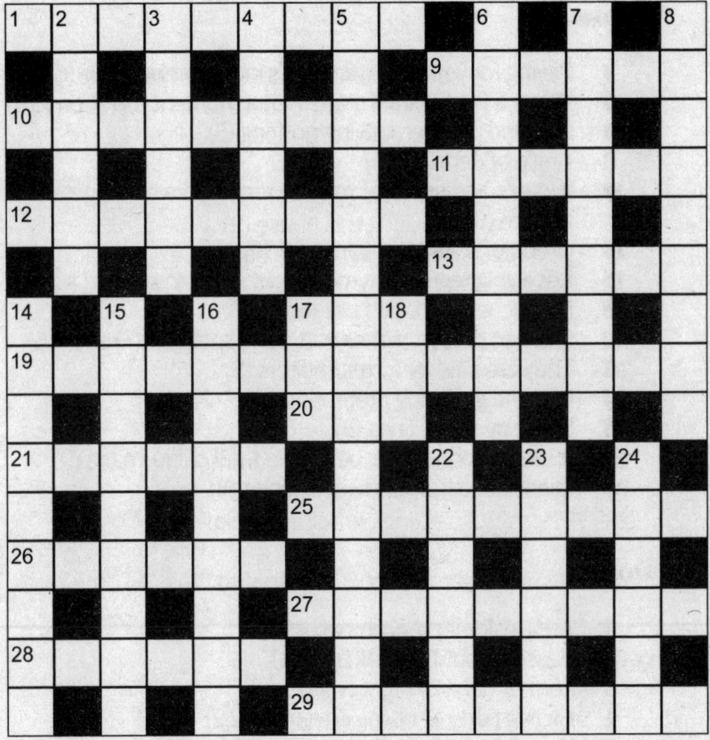

18 Possessing endless ingenuity (3)
22 Get back from playing area with love in the air (6)
23 Frisky setter's way (6)
24 Boating teams discussed pleasure trip (6)

27

Across

1 Paying for yourself twice – it's incomprehensible (6,5)
9 When a fight should start? Not a moment too soon (5,4)
10 Live and prosper, lacking nothing (5)
11 Angle of density? (6)
12 Writer's addition that may be removed when it gets to the theatre (8)
13 Group of soldiers in particular (6)
15 Receiving regular payments, disposed to give lad a rise (8)
18 Production of Haydn's oratorio (8)
19 Learned person makes witticism, spoken in French (6)
21 They are paid by formal visitors (8)
23 Boy and girl being pretentious (2-2-2)
26 Some overseas lines (5)
27 A bloomer he made, being too fond of his image (9)
28 Minds centre around intelligence (11)

Down

1 Area inside American bases (7)
2 Vessel about to break up (1-4)
3 Former habit of night work? (4,5)
4 Having party at home is murder (2,2)
5 He paints badly but he can act (8)
6 Avoid commitment that's about agricultural land, perhaps (5)
7 Slackened, becoming loose in a rush (7)
8 It's a blow that has to be faced (8)
14 Worship money (8)
16 To laud in a new excess of flattery (9)
17 Satisfies all within (8)
18 Two vehicles joined by a third one (7)
20 Start in winding passage (7)
22 Troops invading England's boundaries? Correct (5)
24 Problem children (5)

25 Charge is about right on the house (4)

Across

1 Rush second spicy dish (6)
4 Uncommonly brave taking Latin oral (6)
8 Jokes about youth leader in room in party clothes (4,4)
10 Endless money in old gaming house (6)
11 Top complete/incomplete? (4)
12 Male prison, dreadfully cold (10)
13 Railway buff instructs one at the wheel? (12)
16 Set about sailor after showing characteristic restraint (12)
20 Legendary female reportedly produced song from *West Side Story*, nervously at first (4,6)
21 Taken initially from large amount in bag (4)
22 Closed trunk as well (2,4)
23 Nato reorganisation unlikely, but don't mention it (3,2,3)
24 Character vandalised tea urn (6)
25 Original piece of cotton fabric in drawer? (6)

Down

1 Royalist abroad, living alone (8)
2 In the process of looting, with place being abandoned (5)
3 Cash in study is dipped into by European (7)
5 Former winner, it's believed, maintains pressure — and that's not all (7)
6 See man in charge bagging runs (9)
7 Secure a posh carriage (6)
9 Son winning place, in theory (11)
14 Batting team dismissed, comprehensively (6,3)
15 Enter provisionally one name below writer (6,2)
17 Clergyman's written about a source of nuclear energy (7)
18 Caretaker to start to repaint after New Year's Day? (7)
19 Colour of satellite orbiting area close to Jupiter (6)
21 Guy eating a Malaysian dish (5)

29

29

Across

7 Make the most of saying one's right of course (8)
9 Pasta nut (6)
10 Responsibility – it's our treat! (4)
11 A crust for father's endeavour following promotion? (4,6)
12 Some said I put savings back, being daft (6)
14 Backing tabloid, captures awards (8)
15 The old old chap? A farmer in times gone by (6)
17 A year in ghetto's refuge (6)
20 Programme chosen to include the Spanish steps (8)
22 Meal of mushy peas in empty restaurant (6)
23 Little girl gets second testimonial to give out (10)
24 Small container routed through west of Liverpool (4)
25 Prime Minister rejecting fish after a case of treatment (6)
26 Illegal occupant, short and stocky, they're regularly chasing (8)

Down

1 Anchor showing unusual stamina, say – finally (8)
2 Works, lacking time for paintings (4)
3 Went quickly, getting bitten (6)
4 Fires half of main agents protecting king (8)
5 Fish batter covering last of chips is rubbish (10)
6 Legendarily careless cook's adder flan partly sent back (6)
8 Guy perhaps having topless challenge eating fruit (6)
13 Scheme and lie about rocket, for example (10)
16 Spray from a cat is here inside (8)
18 Young lady admits gate money errors (8)
19 Points of contention in numbers (6)
21 Feature on head of this zoo losing specs for material (6)
22 Primate's right hand suppressing potential uses (6)
24 Run checks on opening of Olympic bar (4)

30

30

Across

1 Film abandoned after indigestion? (4,4,3,4)
9 Care when news is broadcast? Negative reaction with it returning (9)
10 Ornamental wear shown by trio at rear oddly (5)
11 First clue about son, a son of Abraham (5)
12 Around back of cabin, note tiny rambling insignificant type (9)
13 Easily taken in with part of hotel bill (ugly!) on reflection (8)
14 Calm Frenchman taken with the Home Counties? (6)
16 Basic commodity like corn getting soft inside (6)
18 Malicious damage got a base upset (8)
22 Better element in bunch providing most important figure (3,6)
23 Look and dress shown by round character (5)
24 Doze in middle of duty? That's not in keeping (5)
25 A place for experimenting with flower as ornamental material (9)
26 Precautions a team, not English, organised? Much fuss about nothing (1,5,2,1,6)

Down

1 Crusty dish associated with good bars? (7)
2 Practice session before dance and sport (7)
3 Players attending companion, sick fellow, with, perhaps, extra indication of cold? (4-5,6)
4 Instrument that could be eternal? (8)
5 Neaten anteroom's interior for temporary dweller (6)
6 Notice leader moving behind part of hospital in historic agreement (7,8)
7 Fancy a drink among fruit left out (7)
8 Sad expression in two notes by a male in East Sussex town (5,2)
15 Princely sort quite open facing a poor actor in turn (8)

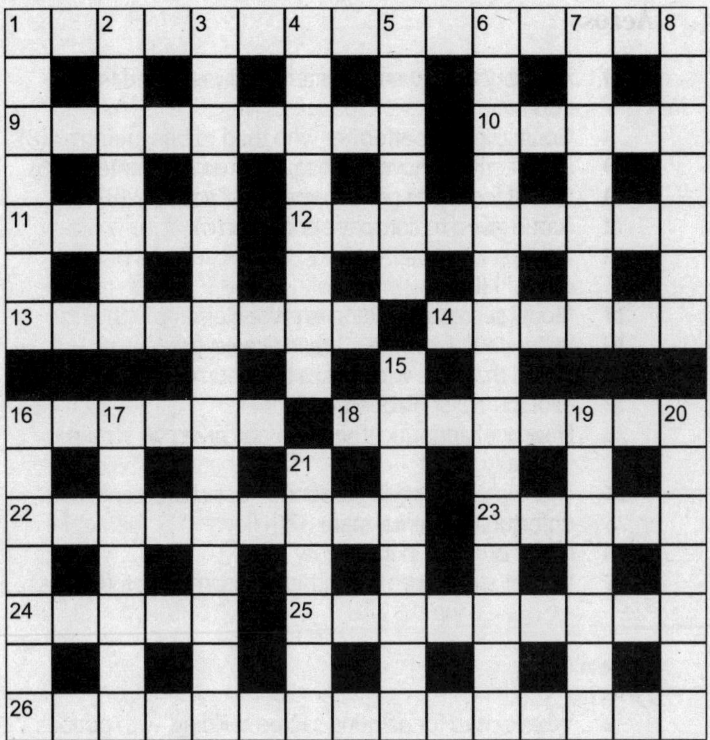

16 Fruit is a necessity when heading north (7)
17 Road covering, a wintry safety measure for traffic round Portsmouth's outskirts (7)
19 Austere figure in a southern church with nervous habit (7)
20 European received grave letters for selfish conduct (3-4)
21 I'm unfortunately upset to get seasoned meat (6)

Across

1 A victory with two characters finally released from court (6)
5 Gong given to performer who tried to bring reform? (8)
9 Party activity shows such racialism unfortunately (7,6)
10 Sort of footballer put off when goal goes in? (8)
11 Name given to complete crackpot (6)
12 The first character to preach (the result of a burning desire?) (6)
14 Model secretary holding everyone else up? (8)
16 In the course of fights thrash Greeks (8)
19 Wood that gets walked in a lot in summer? (6)
21 Idiot journalist blabbered (6)
23 How brief announcement may be given on screen suddenly (2,1,5)
25 One Irish chap jigging around — last character in that unfortunate mental state (13)
26 Name of nurse in Italian city (8)
27 Violent street with wicked leader bumped off (6)

Down

2 What's used for painting sacred building, with pounds spent on artist (7)
3 Spring edition (5)
4 Country club joined by academic, international ace (9)
5 Criminal pair one found in sect (7)
6 Like layer that's very pale (5)
7 Half of them on trail collapsing in demanding race (9)
8 Dubious American Pastor in dissenting body (7)
13 One extending a provision for injured players (9)
15 Savage acts bringing terrible scare to large number (9)
17 Soldier only briefly gets overhead protection (7)
18 Block a series of steps with two pianos? That looks dotty! (7)

32

20 Drunk sat in a part of the wine cellar – to kick his habit? (7)
22 A number practise a form of Buddhism (5)
24 Ship is tarry, not good (5)

Across

1 Cutter was turning jade first (7)
5 Fool of a son taken in by knaves (7)
9 Being in charge one needs to be straight (5)
10 Person investigating artist has cut round to enter uninvited (9)
11 Athlete has try to join club (4-6)
12 Wild plant may be watered! (4)
14 Common freedom enjoyed by Dusty (3-2-3-4)
18 The royal couple in grand flirtation (12)
21 German song was deceptive (4)
22 Dressed like priest, one may get profit (10)
25 Who's abandoned seat in bar? (9)
26 Italian with alluring air oddly rejected (5)
27 Lugubrious donkey's slightly rearranged hideous thing (7)
28 Trap for criminals set by volunteers, getting a nibble (7)

Down

1 The woman's promiscuous — not a minority view (6)
2 Herbivore eating everything that's green (6)
3 Rap cults mad about religious instruction according to the Bible (10)
4 Island where boat crew changes direction at the start (5)
5 One widely travelled black dog (3-6)
6 Company taking care of palm tree (4)
7 Directed a chartered accountant to make cutback in universities (8)
8 List including first of down clues he rehashed (8)
13 Kansas belt turned out abnormally tall plants (10)
15 Artillery keeping independent regulation (9)
16 What's fallen out from small sack (8)
17 Landlord with infestation seen redeveloping (8)
19 Something valuable in one's house (6)
20 Police leader once detaining first of race horses (6)

23 Feel sorry for headless bird (5)
24 Decline old pudding (4)

33

Across

1 Clean motor off to get set for a rally? (5,5)
9 It produces high sound if turned up (2-2)
10 The greatest amount of pride? (5,5)
11 Office workers go to a Scottish island (6)
12 Methods intended to avoid betting slips? (7)
15 One's young and in form (7)
16 Many wager on the return of this ship (5)
17 A girl is after one, right? (4)
18 African menagerie's toilet, say? (4)
19 Exhaust advice on employment of umbrellas (3,2)
21 Rude and very Scottish sort of hut (7)
22 Tragically be match for a Shakespearean hero (7)
24 Gold glow of chestnut (6)
27 The tears we shed for a loved one (10)
28 Make an impression as an artist (4)
29 I tell tutor about one spreading rubbish (6,4)

Down

2 Party rising in power in old Scandinavia (4)
3 Money box of very poor quality? (3-3)
4 Regular habits and duties (7)
5 Old Spanish coin about a pound (4)
6 The easiest dance to learn? (3-4)
7 It's more fun tussling in adversity (10)
8 A money-making contact (5,5)
12 Let us admit becoming excited (10)
13 Return to a fairground attraction? (10)
14 Cut Sophia Loren's initials on a tree (5)
15 A substitute for healing, perhaps (5)
19 Pan, you sound unusually silent (7)
20 Handy place for a painter to mix his colours (7)
23 Just happened to be wicked (6)
25 Note the amphibian is adroit (4)

34

26 Some favour Dutch as a language (4)

Across

1 Love to paddle back large boat (7)
5 What cricketers might do, say? (7)
9 More annoyed from breaking earring (7)
10 Soldier returned: no communist's overlooked (7)
11 Steel smashed policeman by bottom of bridge – it might make one see stars! (9)
12 Private meal with no starter (5)
13 Cart reversing by small enclosed spaces (5)
15 Right inside a chimney, uprooted plant (9)
17 One who gives orders, upset nerd (9)
19 Bottle never drunk (5)
22 A minor prize (5)
23 Got together and strolled around Sussex regularly (9)
25 Pale, one doesn't take part in battle (7)
26 Scoffing servicemen get old in dispatch (7)
27 What brides might put on grooms (7)
28 Regret impertinent talk about heads of department needing education (7)

Down

1 Loaded rifles the law destroy in the end (7)
2 Soldier's uniform (7)
3 Awful rash around centre of his whiskers (5)
4 Put on knitted jumper for media (9)
5 Rubbish left out where car is parked, perhaps (5)
6 Prisoner I'd picked up bashed into shape (9)
7 A teacher's last selection for class (7)
8 Old tree lay hollowed-out (7)
14 Dad's rants breaking protocol (9)
16 Noel Edmonds finally involved in its March broadcast (9)
17 Bound criminal in each dungeon, initially (7)
18 This compiler has a certain restraint (7)
20 Free album, for example (7)

35

21 Everlasting conclusions about the French (7)
23 It shows you places a sailor's turned up (5)
24 Entertained without a thought (5)

Across

1 Stop believer adopting son (6)
4 When to make an illegal copy of such a letter (8)
10 Cry, seeing potential partner wrapped in fleece (4,1,4)
11 Picture that is printed on exterior of magazine (5)
12 Won't he gossip about moving? (2,3,2)
13 Candidate free of explosive energy? (7)
14 Girl who's almost conventional? (5)
15 Award a medal for dress? (8)
18 Resist unfinished bedding, though free (8)
20 Sentimental start after letter from Athens (5)
23 Plain Vichy water by factory with no name (7)
25 In France no way work is constant (3-4)
26 Put a coat on and look around west of London (5)
27 Greeting workers with fish (9)
28 Written study for disposal of batteries with no lead (8)
29 Dearie me! The French are barracking (6)

Down

1 Get off on smut, worried after I'd returned (8)
2 Garment for person feeling the heat? (7)
3 Trip out for king supporting women in new palaces (9)
5 Bound to get strange glance in seasonal brush-up? (6-8)
6 Expression from endless fool getting married (5)
7 Opposing a profit on site, oddly (7)
8 Old film with Queen in West Country city (6)
9 Support ideas causing change of heart (6,8)
16 Remember soldiers and dresses before church (9)
17 Fitted lens from storm centre on gun (8)
19 Not knowing some run a war economically (7)
21 Disappointment of some tennis support (7)
22 Peg rings regularly in place (6)
24 Stand before court (5)

36

Across

1 Execution of play at the end with a twist (5,7)
8 Jacked up without one getting demolished (5)
9 Queen's back, refined with rap (9)
11 Repelled by North American consumed about nosh (9)
12 Tickle trout's tail with dexterity (5)
13 Catch terrible cheat causing anguish (9)
16 Time sprint for dash (5)
18 Loose woman, one related, going topless (5)
19 Supple, candlelit, he sometimes embraces (9)
20 Declare opening securing maiden (5)
22 Leaving helpless redhead in station (9)
25 Sailor at sea, some say, descending by rope (9)
26 Batsman ends suppressing naked muscularity (5)
27 Let bra settle perhaps giving temporary support (7,5)

Down

1 He may argue policeman's set on worker (9)
2 Count on the French to get confused (5)
3 Wood shed contains fearsome interior (5)
4 Former wife on exercise regime including new method (9)
5 Happen to swallow slug left for philosopher (9)
6 Elevated skill including top female accessory (5)
7 African gnu he shot in foreign region (6,6)
10 Motor stops on European railway – English shortly coming aboard (6,6)
14 Smash hit recast for performance (9)
15 In grace, lest I allow heart's divine (9)
17 Loathe a bad smell friend holds in (9)
21 One embracing one's tender? (5)
23 Initially redacted original great English thesaurus (5)
24 Tycoon and toff pocketing a billion (5)

37

37

Across

5 Time to get a round in concert – find the bar (7)
7 The fellow protected by idiot remains (5)
9 One embraced by enthusiast at church – he may go there to get wed (6)
10 Obstructive, with a yen to be different (2,3,3)
11 Warning politician, I'd moan terribly at the start (10)
13 I proceed to grab a villain (4)
14 One club redesigned with format not conducive to relaxation (13)
16 Confront female expert (4)
17 New car with Cellnet that can deal with phone messages (4,6)
19 Canons in cold form of worship look retrogressive (8)
20 Like many a favourite relation, strange at first (4-2)
22 Male on water? Yes, yes! (5)
23 Cunning vision that accommodates the French (7)

Down

1 Second joke presented by someone using words craftily? (4)
2 Only Conservative is beginning to make error (8)
3 You want kitchen vessel? Then go where the food's kept (6)
4 Finally throw end of loaf that is black in recycling container? (7,3)
5 Chord one gets in a type of jazz (5)
6 Joan takes Isle of Man road the wrong way (4,2,7)
8 Special corner, a bright spot (7)
12 Bands on the move in others' cars (10)
14 Like a secret opinion that's stuffy? (7)
15 After sign of approval maiden perhaps becomes idle (4,4)
17 Former President in vehicle with Her Majesty (6)
18 Australian mammals need time to find shelter (5)

38

21 Accommodation evoking snide comments (4)

Across

1 Head of department drops alternative claim (7)
5 Bags to carry new light bites (6)
9 Amphibian, male, Rex found in the gloom (8)
11 Ethical drug gives confidence (6)
12 Rejection for ex-GI band (4)
13 The abstract art I state to be spectacular (10)
14 Agents' damage mended and dramatically arranged (5-7)
17 Hardy product maybe that could be shelved (8,4)
21 Gloomy writer to make cuts (4-6)
22 Bridge partners holding ace and five, producing movement by Queen, perhaps? (4)
23 A pungent bulb, left out, can generate fungus (6)
24 Solitary slapdash cavalier (8)
25 Farm machine mysteriously departed after father retired (6)
26 Wandering tale of donkey's years being unconventional with Karen dropping out (7)

Down

2 Course taken about permit needed for gambling game (8)
3 Sheet of oil shimmering (5)
4 Rock band (7)
6 Means of identification guard turned up (4,3)
7 A crowd meandering about gain access to a moving view (3,6)
8 Ottoman leader will get no end of fruit (6)
10 Environmentally friendly shopkeeper? (11)
15 Odder, long hybrid plant (9)
16 High level ground rent (8)
18 Unfinished tea includes clear liquid syrup (7)
19 Newsman following race broadcast (7)
20 Escape journey made by air (6)
22 Cut up about the European country (5)

39

Across

1 Pay attention to sermon? (7)
5 Goes into a long-term partnership (7)
9 The pack must return to desert (5)
10 Butter and milk producer (5,4)
11 Shrank from being engaged (10)
12 Dances with instruments in the toolroom (4)
14 It provides a good base for an evening out (7-5)
18 A challenging demand (12)
21 General assistant (4)
22 Hunt for a drink? Just the opposite (7,3)
25 Advocate for a famous explorer gaining essential point (9)
26 Run away with East European on the rebound (5)
27 Following points go to the prosecution (7)
28 Uncommon pronoun (5,2)

Down

1 Charge for illness (6)
2 Attorney to call for defiance (6)
3 Come in force, showing initiative (10)
4 Describing noise of icons breaking (5)
5 Food from the earth – £500 to an aficionado (6,3)
6 Fish to breed, say (4)
7 Sarcastic driver possibly in charge over a learner (8)
8 Adjourn tennis match with scores level? (3,5)
13 You bet positively (10)
15 Almost object: 'That could have caused an accident' (4,5)
16 Inserted plug in leak – a daring exploit (8)
17 Academic bosses admit financial liability (8)
19 Where porpoises are taught? (6)
20 Field the ball (6)
23 It's essential to a helicopter going up or down (5)
24 Note uprising of W African tribe in desert (4)

40

40

Across

1 Punishment? Why? (4,3)
5 Colonist, one taking part in landing (7)
9 Item initially pinched by the female cat burglar (5)
10 Hears about ancient disasters (9)
11 Keep following film director in retreat… (5,5)
12 …to check shoot (4)
14 Motorway's appearance is wrong (12)
18 Pole has lodgings by Welsh river (12)
21 Singer in musical, *Tommy* (4)
22 Girl in rhyme sits with me, worried about what will keep hands warm (4,6)
25 Popular person, modern and lively, coming from ball at cricket club (9)
26 Charge across river for bait (5)
27 Drive off to bring adult member in for massage (7)
28 Goody-goody in up-train, unsettled (7)

Down

1 Up-to-date intelligence prior to strike (4,2)
2 A small key (1,5)
3 Shared in centre of Dallas, capitally? (5-5)
4 Old-style resort abroad devoid of sun (5)
5 Collect dull rug (6,3)
6 Finished extra six deliveries (4)
7 Absurd notice about six getting the push (8)
8 Herb sprang up, one good with lamb? (8)
13 Watch Attila? (4-6)
15 Slipping up, party after daughter's heroic action (7-2)
16 Song from *Hair* stars (8)
17 Animated film freak is at a resort (8)
19 A launch at sea (6)
20 Last broadcast by elected Soviet leader (6)
23 Abandon fight (5)

41

24 Wet head of wretched scallywag (4)

Across

1 Rump, ham or game? (10)
6 Slump preceding a long tale (4)
8 Fine-tuning of foresight on unloaded rifle (8)
9 The shape of Bologna after most of it is developed (6)
10 Work land area on hill producing food for Mexico (8)
11 Swindle crowd (6)
12 Smile, with time for new determination (4)
14 Done half of this part of the golf course (7)
18 Import from Chinese dynasty to include endless jeans (7)
20 Piece of news one came across on the way back (4)
23 Nothing very loud to establish counterbalance (6)
24 Net value is adjusted, becoming final after a time (8)
25 Chair apparently embracing return of outcast (6)
26 Stubborn, but bound to reform without new charge (8)
27 Hide, if virtually broke (4)
28 People in power panicking at teens on grass (10)

Down

1 Exhausted ticket seller after sting (5-3)
2 Insurance agent's final secret (6)
3 'Shot' — small drink for small talk (6)
4 Doctor performing easy work unofficially (9)
5 They open, exceptionally, for a new convert (8)
6 Drink on board with partner's representative (8)
7 Go to Scotland and put up new fuel nerve centre (8)
13 Inflexible but viable perhaps including two thousand plus order initially (9)
15 Fine line taken in joint request for small container (3,5)
16 Lack of love on religious outpost? (8)
17 Good *Independent* newspaper report for retail outlet (8)
19 Coins once used for drugs lie all over the place (8)
21 Fashionable channel to admit as member (6)
22 Country or kingdom raised women on island (6)

42

Across

1 Kid getting into music roots out old footwear (4,5,5)
9 Gatsby recalled except via a name in books still? (8)
10 Fellow embraces company and wine (5)
12 Hairstyle making a comeback in *Doctor Faustus* (4)
13 Tip off, using good English, about arranged eviction (4,6)
15 Desolate amateur shrink (3,5)
16 Garden rubbish hazard (6)
18 Same two chords in Emerson Lake & Palmer's records (6)
20 Visual humour landmark requires silence (5,3)
23 Bird of prey noticed displaying evidence of conformity (4-6)
24 Marrow in haggis? Turnips apparently (4)
26 High wire safety issue making work for nine (5)
27 One with depression, needing vermouth – unknown brand (8)
28 Head latterly went on about sense and shrewdness of judgment (3-11)

Down

2 Could be Lulworth skipper having abandoned heading misses France completely (7)
3 Wise ignoring half of sausages' ingredients (4)
4 Waste burger one tucked into with energy before (8)
5 Hazel perhaps will follow two directions in course (6)
6 Hospital may hope to offset treatment (10)
7 Take the edge off delightful impression (7)
8 Come a cropper cutting into opening question (11)
11 Austin maybe left benefits protecting popular originator of 1 (4,7)
14 Overdue, Sun taking blame sadly for Jerry Lee Lewis and 11 among others (10)
17 Being on strike for an aid to survival (8)
19 Auntie P rarely reveals her name (7)

43

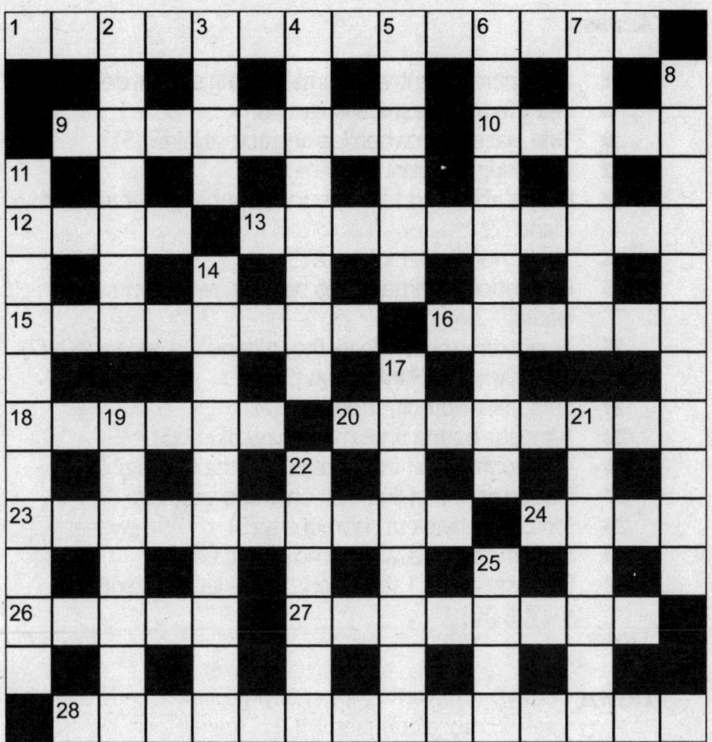

21 Cook – no learner – set grill for rubbery piece of meat (7)
22 Making an effort can be distressing (6)
25 Boss's doubt is not even raised (4)

Across

1 Commercial centre with mail having special delivery (10)
6 Injury in thigh restricting run (4)
9 One place seen when looking across lake? (5)
10 Cue bridging a rest (9)
12 Is legendary bird seen around about a Mediterranean island (7)
13 That's not proper ice stick (5)
15 Revolutionary time has to be right, with commander leading (7)
17 To accommodate dead, the underworld widens out (7)
19 Two games in Hants town (7)
21 Sung part 'notedly superior'? (7)
22 A mostly boring time makes you blue? (5)
24 Unfavourable bit from chapter of the NT, say? (7)
27 Person at end of line misconstrued language (9)
28 Motorway lane cut short in city (5)
29 Dreadful day I recall with no phone (4)
30 Fantastic actor, I star as one of the landed gentry maybe (10)

Down

1 Girl upsetting her best friend, not half! (4)
2 Adopts a different position as elector suffering (9)
3 There's place for sacrifice — change is being mentioned (5)
4 English bishop involved in row is an eager person (7)
5 Old doctor entertained by fat Italian citizen (7)
7 Mountains within American desert (5)
8 Something in steel that makes main street look awful (10)
11 Wild animals naughty child sits on unfortunately (7)
14 Part of what coin counterfeiter must do to speed up successfully? (5,5)
16 Something absorbing in the writer's study? (7)
18 For me level tar may be spread on top of road (9)

44

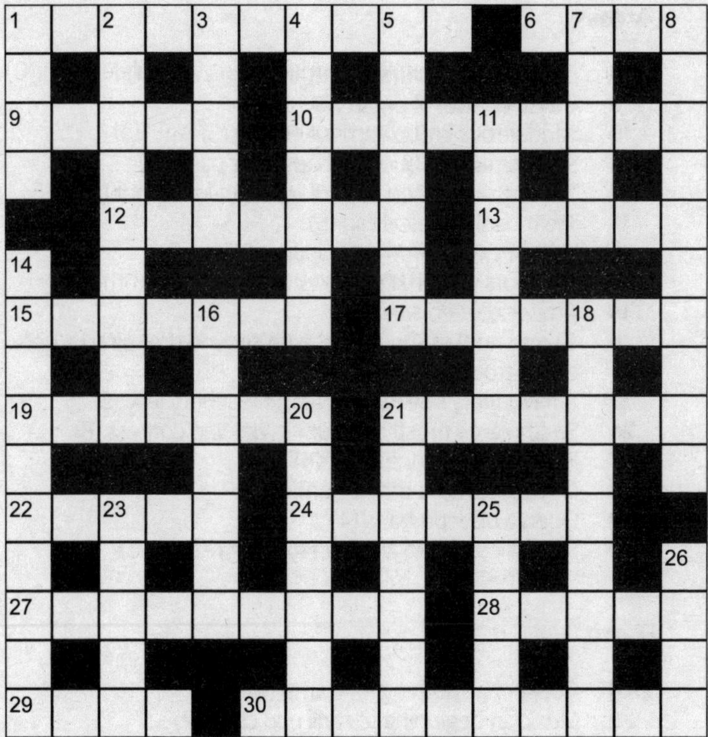

20 Coach is means of transport taken with hesitation (7)
21 I have risen in party – American playing dirty (7)
23 Superior meal but without starter (5)
25 This person in love repeatedly kept under by right lover (5)
26 A negative word being spoken is a difficulty (4)

Across

1 Drink a lot of Spanish wine and turn in (3,3,4)
6 Cease control of organ (4)
10 Sadder rock group without energy (5)
11 Singer makes a buck perhaps after party (9)
12 Turning over when start of update's imminent (8)
13 Treat badly tropical fish (5)
15 Hurtful extract from newspaper (7)
17 One puts up with English vicar (7)
19 Arbiter cooked snack (7)
21 Takes snooker shot again, with second dropping in, gets out of trouble (7)
22 A flavouring, free from Spain, for savoury jelly (5)
24 Smith came mostly unstuck in uneven contest (8)
27 Fashionable thinner bust (9)
28 One agreement that is perfect (5)
29 Open a beer perhaps (4)
30 Send message to artist, an exciting read (4-6)

Down

1 Cooker has nothing for tramp (4)
2 Musician beginning to thrill odd chap (9)
3 Leading man gets new bird (5)
4 Close relative is turning up with jewellery (7)
5 Something to divert traffic round block in German city (7)
7 Source of information for bank robbery (5)
8 Two big hairstyles on street feature up North (10)
9 Keep Usain Bolt's property? (8)
14 Infectious fever leaves mark on South American girl (10)
16 I am having bad feeling about the City, being foolish (8)
18 Stick with rune notch carved (9)
20 Soften a medium (7)
21 Favour being scheduled in routine (7)
23 Crush on a Turkish official (5)

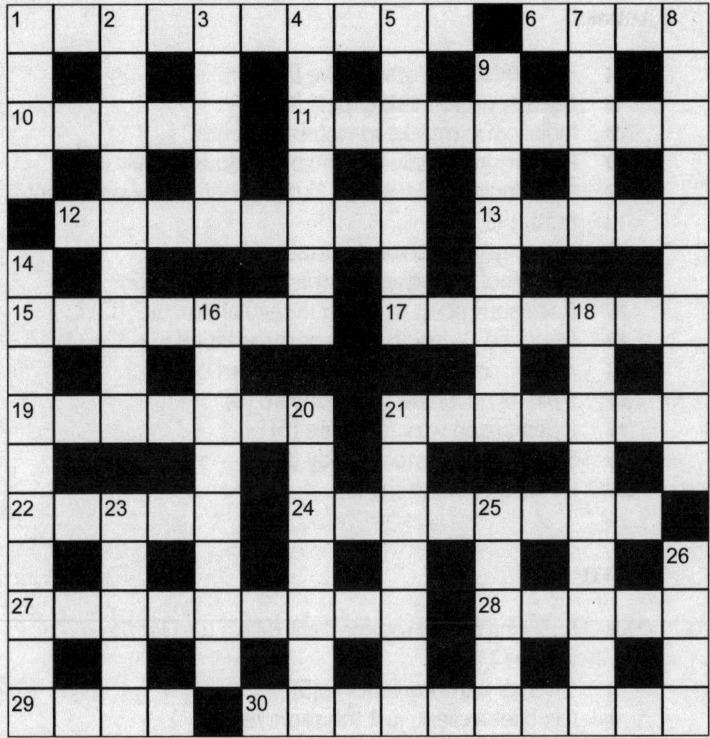

25 Make departure in a university – farewell (5)
26 Slight indistinctness of speech (4)

Across

1 It is difficult being sensitive (8)
6 Build new Northern capital (6)
9 Indian who may keep watch for you (6)
10 Pass, momentarily fail, and break down totally (8)
11 One drink that refreshes, but another will be a different matter (3,2,3)
12 A ship taking trouble to attack (6)
13 Put a foot wrong and he may bail you out (12)
16 A religious point to follow in secular pursuit? (12)
19 Deprived — due to faulty beer measure! (6)
21 As an occupant, I'd resent being put out (8)
23 Swirling mist hides way forward (8)
24 Open prison was adequate (6)
25 Stop and take into custody (6)
26 Held back, being shy (8)

Down

2 Suffering dreary routine, I will take a turn for the worse (2,1,3)
3 Oriental bamboo fencing (5)
4 I'd upset a client, just the same (9)
5 Teacher confused by a metric unit (7)
6 A current issue on the coast (5)
7 Club about to give female support (9)
8 Sad mean-spirited mate left — fired (8)
13 Sorry expression for one banishing the blues (9)
14 Hikers carry these sleeping bags, we hear? (9)
15 Ship carries right pennant (8)
17 He looks after dog on a hill (7)
18 Eventually punctual (2,4)
20 Handle deed without charge (5)
22 Spaniard, or anyone with a gift (5)

46

16

Across

1 Fruit, queen's choice (8,4)
8 Produce mostly stiff undergarment (7)
9 A gauzy fabric under discussion (2,5)
11 Copper is at home with English style of cooking (7)
12 Revolving handle getting a note to emerge (7)
13 United aware of Everton's lead (2,3)
14 Band of gold artist put round part of the trunk (9)
16 Start to back small new broker (2-7)
19 Daily delivery, primarily beet (5)
21 Ailment comes from cool headland, blowing cold and hot (7)
23 One giving better advice? (7)
24 Cocky type rounded hill, was almost captured (4-3)
25 One in cartel amended clause (7)
26 Old German, down delivering a pigment (8,4)

Down

1 Dizziness? I turn green first (7)
2 Before start of Easter, dispenser's short shift (7)
3 Honest one managed to win (2,3,4)
4 Furious, freebooter having lost power (5)
5 Archbishop, strait-laced, dined (7)
6 Social climber put out, interrupted by celebrity (7)
7 Family doctor elected to cut mass of thick hair, a vivid colour (8,4)
10 Jewel adding fresh colour (7,5)
15 Force prisoners on to coach (9)
17 Number giving support to revolutionary Labour prime minister (7)
18 A classic article on timber trees (3,4)
19 Excellent Havana, for example (7)
20 Join European diplomat (7)
22 Conductor turned up in Kuwait, lost (5)

47

17

Across

1 Delicate feminine line (5)
4 Meeting welcoming European Community withdrawal (9)
9 Recover one's senses and drop in (4,5)
10 Agreed to make reparation (5)
11 On the way back, hurried one's drink (7)
12 Locks in canal at Cheshunt (7)
13 Possible horrible environment for sailor (6)
15 Unusual find full of seldom-encountered radiation (8)
18 Getting to every single home within the boundaries of Reading (8)
20 Scoundrel ordered two grand! (3,3)
23 Worried constantly by son getting caught (7)
24 Possible cure for personal problem on site (7)
26 Overnight accommodation with time for student composition (5)
27 A rate adjustment in account involving two sides (9)
28 Fixed and strange manner during hissy fit! (9)
29 Step up, for a bit of fear is erotic (5)

Down

1 One's reputation maintained by this aspect, barring right (4-5)
2 A marine journalist with weapons (5)
3 Racially diverse, excepting one area that's poetic (7)
4 Slight case of remarkably liquid waste on the farm (6)
5 Cooking two fish, including starter of dips (8)
6 Spread some across cat terminally (7)
7 Train for films in America? (4,5)
8 Wants note emailed without contents before start of school (5)
14 Stone and basalt are different (9)
16 In which the vicar takes the lead? (3,6)
17 Unbelievable, denying credit for such food (8)

48

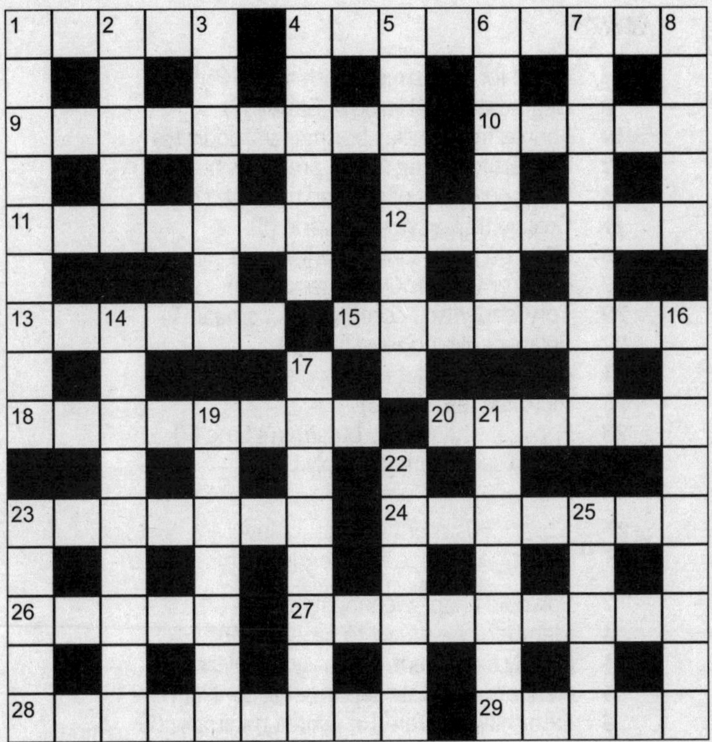

19 A meal that might be off, with side incomplete (4,3)
21 Device putting suitable ruler under notice (7)
22 Pages in a permit for computer program (6)
23 Total of uranium found in oil deposit (3,2)
25 Discovers missing leader and makes money (5)

Across

1 Breed for long stretch with speed (11)
9 Degradation of Herod in Galilee (7)
10 Shrinks from bullies boxing ears, oddly (6)
12 Dessert following recipe produces beams (7)
13 Feast on heads of sea and river fish (7)
14 Groove trailing street parade (5)
15 Idiots do vocal turn for judging (9)
17 Show envy after Queen record (9)
20 Tory leader isn't commonly for smear (5)
22 Relatives like housing free (7)
24 Craftsman in part is a novice (7)
25 Victorian female? (6)
26 Spoils, losing wicket, batsman's time (7)
27 Star in spot orating terribly (11)

Down

2 Splendid chaps wearing right togs (7)
3 Member, one's slow to pass law (9)
4 Initially fix on centre, usually significant (5)
5 Honours socialists suppressing conflict (7)
6 Extremities covered in winter, minimally (7)
7 Mundane river ends in River Test (11)
8 Conservative with tender for treasury (6)
11 Importance of Genesis with new version (11)
16 Job involves travelling to Tunisia (9)
18 He gasps embracing hot 'cougar' (7)
19 One favours best English literature first (7)
20 Eat nuts developing medical condition ... (7)
21 ... for nuts it's silly eating seconds (6)
23 Sun babe turned up accepting new vulgarism (5)

49

Across

1 How deranged, mad, obstinate and perverse! (5-6)
7 Gather after expected time having come to mountain pass (7)
8 University lecturers are briefly entertained by theologian who isn't bright? (7)
10 No performance in church for this piece of music (8)
11 Rows initiated by cold obsessive folk (6)
13 Thanks repeated and so long (2-2)
14 Fellow wanting work, right manipulative type (10)
16 Criticising innocent person — a police trap? (10)
18 Military commander has some bag handlers (4)
21 A service provided by ancient headmaster of yesteryear (6)
22 Green crop either side of river is stuff that's wasted (8)
24 One getting away, see, disguised around head (7)
25 Unfashionable actors in the wilderness? (7)
26 They may make brief drops, ending with 'takeaway' (5,2,4)

Down

1 Unofficial act we might deduce? (7)
2 Obscure old memorial tablet with line missing (6)
3 Jealous person in political organisation (5,5)
4 Is inclined to reject leader's aims (4)
5 Food shop that's odd has one in a state of agitation (8)
6 German article collecting water that facilitates drying process (7)
7 Unruly local teens gathered round end of street in cluster (11)
9 Mad man tries to shoot — weapon removal is the answer (11)
12 Make quiet argument that mathematicians can't refute? (10)
15 One that's enormous as a hit-maker (8)

50

17 Motorway arrest with one having top speed in that vehicle (7)
19 Mr Cooper has managed to get locked in storehouse (7)
20 Dupe the childminder? (6)
23 Every shrubbery has two such insects (4)

Across

1 Demonstrator caught in a short fall of rain? (6)
9 Strait-laced teacher first's scarf (4-6)
10 Beast you'll remove without question (10)
11 Swimmer with a tailpiece (4)
12 Buzz following check, initially, and mate (4)
14 Lasting impression conveyed by grafter – 'I'm a genius!' (5-5)
17 Doctor with a staff shortage that's severe? (7)
18 And in France learn about being immortal (7)
20 Real Madrid's jinking winger (3,7)
21 Crowd – I'll get out of lift (4)
22 Not happy with this record on so late! (4)
23 Little imp returned in passing (5-5)
25 It captures a moving scene (4,6)
26 Air display (6)

Down

2 Obsession with falcon seen above mount (5-5)
3 Get in first round in boozer (4)
4 Complaint of one in fancy summer hat (10)
5 Royalty for joke delivered within 31 days (7)
6 The spy is losing this watch (4)
7 Command – fast over 31 days (5,5)
8 Composed and delivered number loudly (6)
13 Badly suited maiden is game, Edward concluded (10)
15 Rodent catcher allowed to go in rickety vehicle (10)
16 Ruminant's face covering plant (5-5)
19 Twisted about and fleeced (7)
20 Excitable seducer fails to initiate contract (6)
23 Second comic's loot (4)
24 Man coming up from provinces (4)

51

1	2		3		4	■	5	■	6	■	7	■	■	8
■		■		■	9									
■		■		■		■		■		■		■	■	
10										■	11			
■		■	■	■		■		■	■	■		■	■	
12			13	■	14				15				16	
■		■		■		■		■		■		■		■
17							■	18						
■		■		■		■	19	■		■		■		■
20										■	21			
	■	■		■	■	■		■		■	■	■		■
22				■	23						24			
	■	■		■		■		■		■		■		■
25										■		■		■
	■	■		■		■		■	26					

The Telegraph

Across

1 Applications for injury benefit, perhaps (11)
9 Chap soundly digs his plot, he's remembered today (3,6)
10 If damp it's unlikely to make much impact (5)
11 Turning balls that may offer chances (6)
12 Dogs, idle in disposition, will be put out (8)
13 Goes easy – Mabel's upset (6)
15 Certainly in drink – so restrained (8)
18 Is he going in to discover it's all over? (8)
19 Roman sort of light providing sparks (6)
21 Move to a new country home (8)
23 Firework lecture (6)
26 Clothes in season (5)
27 She may take the wheel with dazzling effect (9)
28 The Services may prove decisive in these struggles (11)

Down

1 Garble a broadcast that discovers unknowns (7)
2 The herb season, we hear (5)
3 Gems you can safely handle (9)
4 Weapon for spearing fish? (4)
5 Animated spider in webbing (8)
6 Flapping sails of hemp fibre (5)
7 Multiply without going forth (7)
8 Illegally dispatched (8)
14 Pretentious person turns up, about to light tonight's conflagrations (8)
16 Propose a funny article following serial drama (4,5)
17 Star of the Magic Circle? (8)
18 Slip, perhaps, if up tree (7)
20 Values seem set for a change (7)
22 With revision tries to take the examination again (5)
24 Combination of metals used in common tool (5)
25 A highlight of the night that's clear (4)

52

Across

5 Language used within confines of stag party (7)
7 Old politician going into price for fertiliser (7)
9 Inappropriate, a French affair of honour, unconcluded (5)
10 Develop complex (9)
11 To unsay what has been said about sappers is cowardly (8)
13 Wager involving trouble in lodge (6)
16 That memento, neglected now (2,3,6)
20 Gold on country carriage (6)
21 Where the buffalo roamed, what could provide stew? (4,4)
24 Russian aircraft helping movement of people? (9)
26 Lieutenant suffering setback in match for championship (5)
28 Considered duties to be sorted out by daughter (7)
29 Salad ingredient for fashionable party person short of time (7)

Down

1 Deer kept out of sight crossing southern end of glen (4)
2 Stick a note in this place (6)
3 Bad-mannered male, Italian, entering bar after one (8)
4 Foolish talk over a list (4)
5 Small amount of paper for a country gentleman (6)
6 Beverage teenager brewed (5,3)
7 Essex Man from Harwich, a vulgarian (4)
8 Formal agreement to take out Yemen's leader (6)
12 Measure mountain range (5)
14 Quantity of drink, low in calories, divided by right (5)
15 It's not easy providing a spread indoors? (2,6)
17 Drink, it spilled over a girl (3,5)
18 Alluring island castle (6)
19 Determined, good man approaches English cathedral city (6)

53

22 Told stories, on the way up, about volunteers in army unit (6)
23 Benevolent type (4)
25 Food – good spread (4)
27 Excessively large instrument (4)

Across

1 Show clears up act for broadcasting (11)
9 Dance leader with a star flaring up (5,4)
10 Feature origin of African country (5)
11 Sailor leaves idler to spend (3,3)
12 Not working with film derivative (8)
13 Changed course due to careful handling, say (6)
15 Abandoned pit, chasing good source of profit (4,4)
18 Black sticky stuff from a ship inside breakwaters (8)
19 Birds, for example rest in flight (6)
21 Tried hard, however, welcoming upper-class investor (4,1,3)
23 Heap fury on bishop (6)
26 Time and relaxation needed for rib (5)
27 Having heavy accents, actors go on air (9)
28 Part of house to attract man getting married? (7,4)

Down

1 Stand-in on bed creating a minor story (7)
2 Attempt a bit of personality assessment on the way up (5)
3 People who malign dealers importing duck without wings (9)
4 Dock policeman covering river (4)
5 A source of problems in poor golfer's game (8)
6 People who can be relied on to get shakes (5)
7 Surprise, seeing *Sun* let loose (7)
8 Figure straddling single bed is poison (8)
14 Big girl's up, finding love after pass (8)
16 Ruthless competition to follow trail across limitless heath (3,3,3)
17 Shadow barmen up for replacement (8)
18 Bishop with saint in Rome worried mafia type (7)
20 Level of society putting up *Loose Women* with show of hesitation (7)

54

22 Leading area hotel has regulars in demand (5)
24 Fertiliser rejected during season (August) (5)
25 Nudge up one berry (4)

Across

1 Chain reaction's unstable end? Come off it! (6,6)
9 After drink around mid-afternoon, gets up and staggers (9)
10 Return of a New Age scene (5)
11 On holiday, taking in New York regardless (6)
12 Girl and small fellows say, dress up (8)
13 Airmen flying in aerobatics initially showing fibre (6)
15 Novel girl covering routine, large and rude (8)
18 Ply tense partygoers with Ecstasy (8)
19 Animal back in flat urban surroundings (6)
21 Badly off being run down on street (8)
23 Bring out criminal to be heard? (6)
26 Tedium, being embraced by drunken nuisance (5)
27 Wise to accept Catholic anger for blasphemy (9)
28 Spooks from Shakespeare's opening moving centre stage (6,6)

Down

1 Gloom somehow spread around Italy (7)
2 Drunk compiler's admitted boob (5)
3 Rodent following piper finally in childlike story (9)
4 Stand for artist endlessly showing dexterity (4)
5 Fat Elvis performed for party (8)
6 Group with grand ringing sound (5)
7 Incumbent Obama to lose power? (8)
8 Pet concerns over school head (6)
14 Sweet subsidy supporting female artist (8)
16 Sensational redhead trouble in affair (9)
17 Mugs almost offended judge (8)
18 One tries hanging over bed (6)
20 Characters from literature (7)
22 Sit keeping one's composure (5)
24 Leader of commercial bank's honest (5)
25 Sabbath music fan sort of singing (4)

55

1		2		3		4		5		6		■	■	■
	■		■		■		■		■		■	7	■	8
9									■	10				
	■		■		■		■		■		■		■	
11						■	12							
	■	■	■		■	■	■		■	■	■		■	
13		14				■	15			16				
■	■		■		■	17	■		■		■		■	■
18								■	19					20
	■		■	■	■		■	■	■		■	■	■	
21				22				■	23			24		
	■		■		■		■	25	■		■		■	
26					■	27								
	■		■		■		■		■		■		■	
■	■	■	28											

Across

1 It's 'ruined by the abrader' ? (10)
6 Capital city that is held by king very briefly (4)
10 Trainee given whip, having collected low exam grades (5)
11 Cocoa I'll have initially drunk – I really want the harder stuff! (9)
12 Like someone wearing tartan unable to act? (2,5)
13 One who is sleeping won't be doing much for the business (7)
14 Promising to study quietly inside when there's heavy stuff to digest (5,7)
18 Pursuit of public schoolboys with abnormally low mental age (4,4,4)
21 Get flung around in middle of mess produced by floods (7)
23 Port sending granite abroad (7)
24 One holds booze in chest protected by electronic sounding device (9)
25 Indian people invading mountain castle (5)
26 Part of actor's register in speech (4)
27 Navy led by head that's friend acting like a father (10)

Down

1 Sort of expert breaking the ice (6)
2 Edit revolutionary piece of legislation (6)
3 Taking a direct line with sales force needing to be sorted out (2,3,4,5)
4 Be without post after First in Biochemistry? It's a crime! (9)
5 In summary, harvest has been interrupted by cold (5)
7 Unfortunate home – middle of floor is in a state (8)
8 There's little good in dreadful avarice evident in minister's home (8)
9 Irishmen did not get confused by modern TV feature exciting viewers? (5,9)
15 Gape naughtily, having got there after flipping? (4,5)

56

16 Pay tribute to soldiers, joined by MP maybe (8)
17 Older egg is bad? Nonsense! (8)
19 Public revenue's beginning to fail — is serenity curtailed? (6)
20 Day the heavens may appear to be lively (6)
22 Brown bit of flower cut short, one inside (5)

Across

1 House worker perhaps, I toil furiously in dreadful panic (10)
6 Writer of plays safe for audience (4)
9 Bird needs a moment, being fabulous (10)
10 Person in charge succeeded initially in pitch (4)
12 Incline to follow leaderless soldiers and join up (6)
13 Get little beauty outside car (8)
15 Coach in job a 1 Across means to secure delivery (7,5)
18 Labrador pets destroyed building material (12)
21 Athlete – small one making an impression (8)
22 Locality around a grand house (6)
24 Avoid failure to score (4)
25 Perhaps Babe's heart goes to hunter of boar (3-7)
26 Found players (4)
27 Garage gets building concrete materials (10)

Down

1 Strike enforcer takes nothing from coal product in mine (6)
2 Pass up beer in place (6)
3 Control ball aiming for goal in sport (4-8)
4 What cows eat is about right for dairy product (4)
5 A cricket club phone sound cut short in Stanley's place (10)
7 Pilot has crashed – get him here (8)
8 Dignitaries or head of state beset by cats (8)
11 Liberal is redrafting Parliamentary process (5,7)
14 One hungry celebrity covering up – not I (10)
16 Is act arising in long story happening from time to time (8)
17 Loudly criticises accommodation (8)
19 Forwards alien parcel (6)
20 Ruins partly inside Bristol (6)
23 Druggie, Liverpudlian but not Scot mostly (4)

57

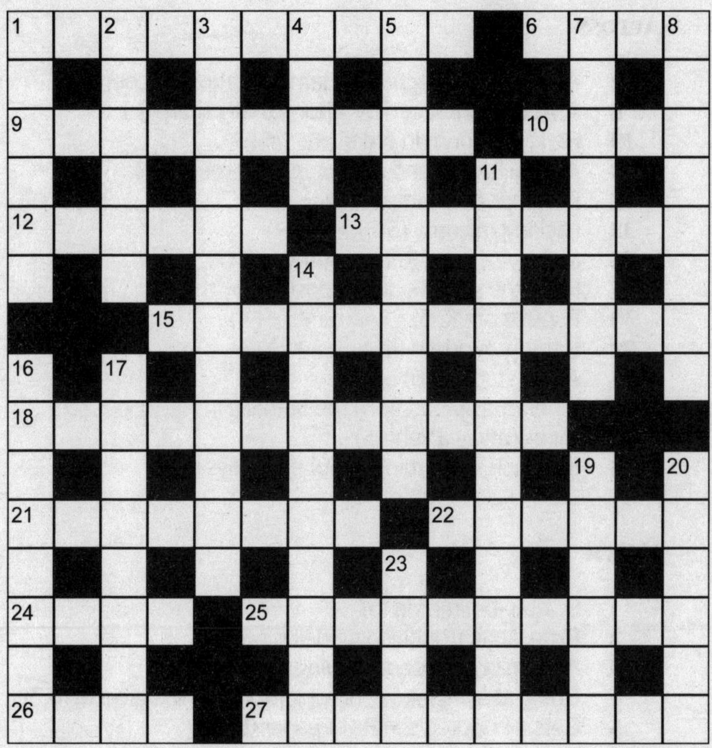

Across

7 Aunt will be affected by demonstration, of course (9)
8 A wound produced by a point that's sharp (5)
10 He keeps mum in order (8)
11 Animal has no end of courage in a melee (6)
12 Fastener for a jumper (4)
13 Lacking majority (5-3)
15 Many years in a Roman Army unit (7)
17 Have the sheriff's unit in position by the ship (7)
20 Popular pro (2,6)
22 Underground TV (4)
25 Ascot starter? (6)
26 Cinerama spread from the States (8)
27 Throw away a fight (5)
28 Stomach is churning – but he enjoys it! (9)

Down

1 Scatter-brain child (5)
2 Extra large, troublesome delivery (6)
3 A gremlin disposed to swing the lead (8)
4 Going at full speed – or lying prone on the ground (4,3)
5 Gets a hundred sheets of paper (8)
6 In two ways, compass is most unorthodox (9)
9 Having been in cooler in police department (4)
14 Increase support to control violence (9)
16 When to have a drink and perhaps eat? (3-5)
18 How the skipper may be caught unawares? (2,3,3)
19 A jolly girl's joined the fighting ships (7)
21 Sign making appeal to males? (4)
23 *Gay Lib* – the novel (6)
24 Girl getting over a fever (5)

58

Across

1 One in seven miners is retiring (7)
9 State induced by depression or trouble (8)
10 Sue is so proper (7)
11 Lump welcomes lunchtime – he likes to fill his face (8)
12 Buffet with beer (6)
13 This gets carelessly misplaced – perhaps too carelessly (10)
15 Ashmolean regularly reviewed charitable donations (4)
16 Are they boring to do this pop trios like? (6,3)
21 All right to uncork wine? (4)
22 Generous care of two French gentlemen provoking hatred (10)
24 Breathe without sound (6)
25 Individually do something with no chance of success (4,4)
27 Putrid concoction stored originally inside hamper (7)
28 Volunteers not drinking before start of dinner, getting ragged (8)
29 A good eighteen holes wrecked (7)

Down

2 'Rocky' a bad role inspiring great affection (8)
3 Close broadcast with no current issue (8)
4 Perfect referee to control Northern Ireland and Austria heading for draw (10)
5 It's nonsense some characters in Branagh's *Othello* are upset (4)
6 Temperature or pressure leads to overriding and ruinous inertia (6)
7 Bound to be hot below opening either side of chimney (7)
8 Born in chirpy milieu of East London (7)
11 See business routinely being as regular as this? (9)
14 One could make strides with this drill possibly (10)
17 Reluctant air settled over gigolo (8)

59

18 Stalks cut back in downward spiral (8)
19 Detective stifled by a town's bitterness (7)
20 Mike interrupting garbled patois that's laid on thick (7)
23 Twerps docked point — or lots (6)
26 *Three Men In A Boat* perhaps vaunted (4)

Across

1 Loyalist beginning to accept law-breaking (8)
6 Sanctimonious and risqué form of stealing (6)
9 Sticker's almost green, dear (6)
10 Clinger-on lost balance crossing river (8)
11 Instruments for pot smokers? (3-5)
12 Positive response by doctor — though initially most sardonic (6)
13 Fork out a wad (dollars), eating fine dish (7,5)
16 Takes out two sailors with energy for beef dish (5,7)
19 Ruined miners oddly missing items of clothing (6)
21 Forceful macho types held in check (8)
23 Name a European working for a military commander (8)
24 Sell fifty per cent share of rare dog (6)
25 Header misdirected — getting stick! (6)
26 Adore old ruined city full of riches (8)

Down

2 Most of gossip is about kid of a particular group (6)
3 Left a dog to drink eagerly (3,2)
4 George perhaps, and Paul too — it is fantastic! (9)
5 Graduates invested in Mexican snack sauce (7)
6 Showing embarrassment after father shaved (5)
7 Commercially-produced mature cheese is up (5-4)
8 Porter's rule for salad (8)
13 Dull ladies mainly accepting a rise is out (9)
14 Turned oars flat — hated reef being turbulent (9)
15 Reference point for the Stars and Stripes, say (8)
17 Income for soldiers on location (7)
18 A French family with daughter showing no mercy (6)
20 Go to court — case of damage being material (5)
22 Drive from heath across top of town (5)

60

Across

7 Dilemma produced by number transported by bike and a railway (8)
9 Regard alike English queen and retired foreign character (6)
10 Superficial flaw in golf shot (4)
11 Copper consuming a second fine drink largely in disguise (10)
12 Bird in a cove fluttering close to boat (6)
14 Fanciful Scot, say, with love for bit of alcohol (8)
15 Irregular feature of Lutheran domicile (6)
17 By the sound of it, locate swimmer (6)
20 Base's upset with drunkard overturning building material? (8)
22 Rupture in river entering part of shoreline (6)
23 Clean motor manufactured in gambling venue (5,5)
24 Gullible fellow, English, trailing Northern Ireland politicians (4)
25 List of business from mature Northern lawyer (6)
26 Tie duly designed around opening to exhibition in festive period (8)

Down

1 Person easily persuaded to linger after raising drink (8)
2 Unexpected game (4)
3 First bit of marketing course producing figure with luck? (6)
4 Object of ridicule in genuine denial of charge (8)
5 Revolutionary device for disposing of nuts? (10)
6 Greek character entertaining leader of Turkey? Sign of shame (6)
8 Servile followers avoiding sun with one Middle Eastern national (6)
13 A lot of interest over girl's musical instrument (10)

61

16 Professional keeping pupils under observation? (8)

18 Extraordinary speed a car right away showed in adventure (8)

19 A guy holding lead to Rottweiler that's wandered off? (6)

21 Parasite in cake? (6)

22 British money originally taken out for protection against the elements (6)

24 Info in that addendum taken back (4)

Across

1 Eagerly grab short sleep in first half of meal (4,2)
5 Vehicles with various escorts going round roundabout (8)
9 How strife is re-enacted within well-marked battle site (8,5)
10 African man embracing one of the Spice Girls (8)
11 Maybe I allowed Cockney woman to be heard (6)
12 Quote from a theologian attached to university church (6)
14 Litter left after the match? (8)
16 Irish priest outside game joining worker gone off naughtily (8)
19 After game, one of the nobs fell asleep (3,3)
21 Position of monuments – not far side of square (6)
23 Athenian at home in any element (8)
25 Noble work (6,7)
26 Country driver (8)
27 Refuse is collected in quiet interval (6)

Down

2 Writer was wounded, bitten (7)
3 Run from street having been nipped by bird (5)
4 Eye-catching concert in part of St Mary's, Paddington? (9)
5 Put backside on article that's pleasant, not totally bad (7)
6 Waste material out from Cornish river (5)
7 One escaping from a time immersed in river – medical care needed (9)
8 You'll see me in trade after butchering (3,4)
13 Rental due to be changed or left alone? (9)
15 Black attire torn with anger? (9)
17 Like the value of property Arab let out (7)
18 A US lawyer keeps quiet in study, showing no emotion (7)
20 Female vocalists heading off – they may be wearing rings (7)
22 Part of plant absorbing a liquid when it's hot (5)

62

24 Agency to provide statistical data (5)

62

Across

2 Hanger-on, one getting behind shelter (4-8)
8 Dash! Old train service goes by ten (4)
9 Rush to get computers, etc, and scarper? (3,3,2)
10 Strung-out Louis must drop round for shot in the arm (8)
11 Student starting late as breadwinner (6)
12 Top rep's book? (10)
13 Six-footer in religious group (6)
16 More than one bird in negligee, seductively (5)
17 Capital of Puerto Rico's leaders with a visitor losing the way (6)
18 High flier's suite? (10)
21 Building not likely to move (6)
23 Expressions of disbelief and surprise, going by island in boat (5,3)
24 Commotion as noisily make tea with a laugh (8)
25 Other ranks generally disheartened by revelry (4)
26 Vocalist drunk on recent tour (12)

Down

1 Feel acute embarrassment for the man supporting court order (6)
2 Training regularly? (9)
3 More than one course that is African sweetcorn (6)
4 Ship's officer's instant true-life representation (5,10)
5 I may be seen in 51 green assorted undies (8)
6 Bouquet is old, that's grim (5)
7 Proof of independent study clubs being held by the First Lady (8)
14 One after another (9)
15 Tenth speaker in musical story (8)
16 Produce family unit price (8)
19 Where a gangster traps US politician (6)
20 Irritate jittery general cut off at rear (6)

63

22 Bear east, fleeing from Brunei in confusion (5)

Across

1 One providing better information from starting price (6,7)
10 He has main control of his craft (7)
11 A learner, say, backing female support in maths subject (7)
12 Meet a famous mountaineer (4)
13 Break arranged for one who works in a hot place (5)
14 Baggage in hold (4)
17 Check votes again in detail (7)
18 There's no performance of *The Peacock* (4-3)
19 Game — and how to score in it (7)
22 Unusually smart do for film eminence (7)
24 Parking place for sport (4)
25 Such law presumably implies a suspended sentence (5)
26 Gem of work taking a line (4)
29 Clothing is torn without intention (7)
30 Liberate one soul in torment (7)
31 Defeated by the elements? (7-6)

Down

2 Girl able to set up a whole lot of dates (7)
3 Concerning the content of certain records (2,2)
4 Dashing chap with exotic tan on cheek (7)
5 Disorderly orderly's place of work, perhaps (2,1,4)
6 Put one's name down for a token (4)
7 Stop English doctor going on Greek ship (7)
8 Prince, a rather unusual royal spouse (9,4)
9 Simple game for relatively well-adjusted groups (5,8)
15 Sand possibly holds uranium in this Arab country (5)
16 Such acclaim as Oval erupts about century (5)
20 Steam-whistle stop? (7)
21 Complete outfit for a small charge (7)
22 Give way and die (7)
23 Mourn ailing old peer (7)
27 Material taken in hand? (4)

64

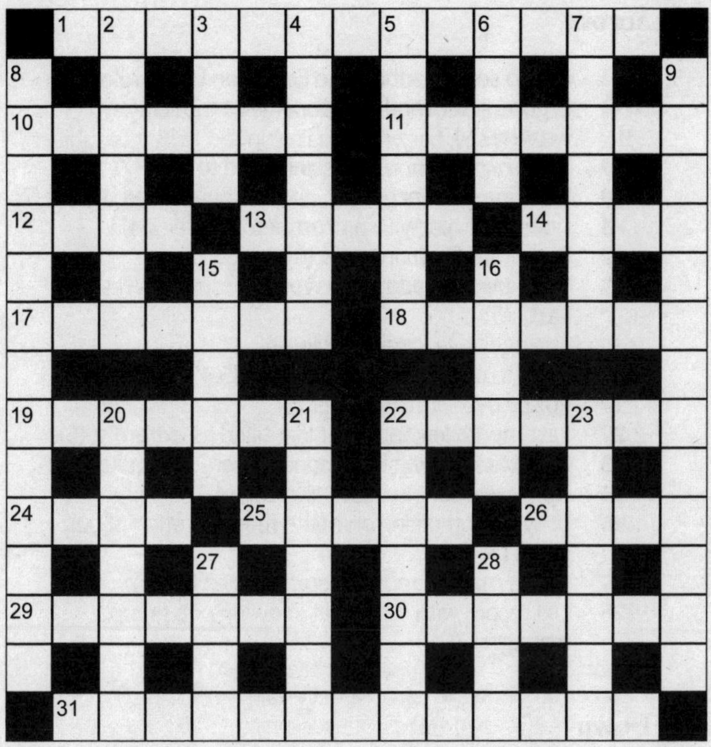

28 She produces articles in Spanish and French (4)

Across

1 Physio service adheres to European Union rule (7)
5 In good health and not working, so moderately wealthy? (4,3)
9 Small number of us on island, hard to feed (7)
10 More inexperienced guy, one out before end of over (7)
11 I joined 14's party to protest before race (5,4)
12 Port – sail from one over in Georgia (5)
13 How one may address a woman from the West or East? (5)
15 The right side leading table (9)
17 Chief to censure bridge contract (5,4)
19 Puzzle over people carrier (5)
22 Last month leading artist identified as extremist (5)
23 Held back playing for second eleven? Not quite (2,7)
25 Upper garment in basin, also cap (4,3)
26 Busy person taking on board reorganisation of quiz game (7)
27 Figure manure must be spread, then left (7)
28 Old record with new inset showing pop group's manager (7)

Down

1 The smallest skirt mother wanted (7)
2 Even daughter agreed (7)
3 Cavell, say, handled it heroically, imprisoned within (5)
4 Learns in the course of proper dummy run (9)
5 Movie star – Rooney, for example (5)
6 Boulanger playing in part of hotel, perhaps (6,3)
7 Material made from angora, woven around back of fez (7)
8 Send on attacking player (7)
14 Tea drinker making foolish threat, animatedly (3,6)
16 Excellent naval officer penning book, second in series (9)
17 Forest creature, a pig (7)

18 An American theatre award going to maiden opposite (7)
20 Nothing inside three-masted vessel is rococo (7)
21 Spotted guarding ambassador and bishop in drinking den (7)
23 One representative the Spanish push forward (5)
24 Classifies courts as redundant (5)

65

Across

1 The lowest point of seabed by Gibraltar… (4,6)
6 …put forward as low point, ultimately (4)
10 Rejects, with no new projections (5)
11 Standard finance should cover exercise book (9)
12 A section of pack ice (8)
13 Gave out late shifts by date (5)
15 Permit put on phone lock (7)
17 Person taken advantage of by troubled dominator not at home (7)
19 Shot the wife to share the cost (2,5)
21 Supporters, of course, eating rotten sweets (7)
22 Distinguish oneself, getting 40 in spoken Latin (5)
24 Underplay but note one's energy (8)
27 Place surrounding unusually green island's national park (9)
28 Substantial part of molecular genetics? (5)
29 Prescribed food that is eaten by dentist with no filling (4)
30 Scientist working more on arts? (10)

Down

1 Knock top off ridge and relax (4)
2 Edged outside to support amusing person warned by police (9)
3 Son in period of prosperity gets a welcoming place (5)
4 One sticks up for maximum rate at sea (7)
5 Resisted quiet model in Oxford, ignoring heart (7)
7 City initially offer millions — what a surprise! (5)
8 Give a lift to work, getting rebuke (4,2,4)
9 Quid pro quo deal on holiday (5-3)
14 Advanced voting system goes red, perhaps around the fifth of August (10)
16 Much less rent by yourself (3,5)
18 Circulating current Moslem art is tricky (9)

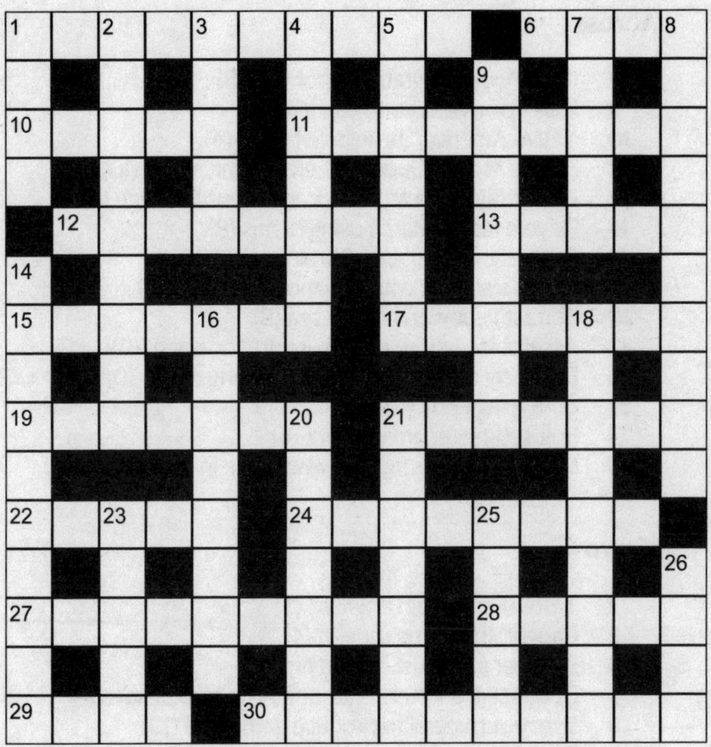

20 People in tents getting hot instead of cold cramps (7)
21 Rebellion of Granite City (7)
23 Swear sulphur is part of remedy (5)
25 Two days lost in Midland city (5)
26 Accept point covered by lawyers (4)

Across

7 Common man grabbing hot bird (8)
9 Bliss from Mathieu to Piaf (6)
10 Native American belief's not dead (4)
11 Enrage former Queen, bit embracing snake (10)
12 I go astray in South American mountain range (6)
14 Players facing match using brains (8)
15 Salutes grand pilot performing roll (6)
17 Bambi's around with one more innocent (6)
20 Retract gear with boat at sea (8)
22 Assembles before court session's opening (6)
23 Endlessly sick patient treated getting clean (10)
24 Bum a fag end? (4)
25 Bolt setting record in sprint (6)
26 Mess for officers fighting resistance in destruction (8)

Down

1 Tasteful porcelain after tea (8)
2 Caught, then time for pen (4)
3 Snapper and artist arrived first (6)
4 Doubt sentence ends around American prisons (8)
5 Turn out mineral to produce gemstone (10)
6 'Beam', part of personnel in *Telegraph* (6)
8 Artist consumed by insides, a shock! (6)
13 Verbose tale or rich fabrication (10)
16 An undergarment dropped in taste for farce (8)
18 Allowance involves old Treasury leader spinning (8)
19 Star of Wimbledon initially getting award (6)
21 Strip for the audience is forbidden (6)
22 Extra performance from Poulenc or Elgar (6)
24 Starts to ban appallingly rowdy sot (4)

67

Across

1 Female member going after half the undergrads – healthy stallions here? (4,4)
9 Look drunk, becoming impenetrable (8)
10 Start to take exercise, casting the first garment (4)
11 The back of Number Ten in the 1950s? A tempting location (6,2,4)
13 When touring around notice various plants (8)
15 Get weary after a short time in formal clothes (6)
16 Chatter in workplace after introduction of bonuses (4)
17 Very good hole in the ground for bird (5)
18 Explorer gets obese, not good (4)
20 Resist work one way and another – set to finish early (6)
21 Mended material put on the clothes-line? (8)
23 Criticism against country that crushes three leaders for democracy (12)
26 A sailor catching fish's tail? He was after something much bigger! (4)
27 Brief conversation with old lover wanting a bit of money? (8)
28 What's upset me twice – lard, bringing a sort of sickness (3,2,3)

Down

2 Very warm current swamping little river (8)
3 George extracted this red resin from tree (7,5)
4 A rodent embracing companion endlessly – where they both escaped flood? (6)
5 Chap contributing to informal entertainment (4)
6 See a goat run around, one on an adventure (8)
7 Not like youngster in prison about to be released (4)
8 Vocalists, including tenor –they can be painful! (8)
12 Entire tax too ridiculous, outrageously high (12)
14 First rate meal that's quiet but not very quiet (5)

68

16 Fish stuck in lake's bottom gets pierced (8)
17 MP I noted being corrupt somewhere in Italy (8)
19 Watch flood engulfing City before end of August (8)
22 Original and unconvincing description of gangster as prudish? (6)
24 Steal from little boy? (4)
25 A skirt's feature that may be used to attract attention (4)

Across

- **1** Lid for a kipper, hot after cooking (4-3,3)
- **6** Returned coats in swindle (4)
- **9** Having regular parts in opera, one singer's a temperamental type (5,5)
- **10** Pleased with cut flower (4)
- **12** Put name to the twins perhaps (4)
- **13** Retreat over rising water is setback for leader (9)
- **15** Follow matters primarily with a habitual response – being this? (8)
- **16** Exemplar of drunkenness regarding famous physicist (6)
- **18** Line to suggest without force (6)
- **20** One in acting role's former model (8)
- **23** Tie up hospital department with attention to detail (9)
- **24** Cattle without water (4)
- **26** European movie, very long (4)
- **27** Seduction ruined eminent 'tec (10)
- **28** Follow story out loud (4)
- **29** A German artist holding opening, one who loves to take risks (10)

Down

- **1** Poet's page to begin poetically (4)
- **2** Making a mockery of barrier (7)
- **3** I may get in maps not fit for easy ride (5,7)
- **4** Mysterious enigmatic coteries (8)
- **5** A free broadcaster (6)
- **7** Piece of Purcell is taxing musician (7)
- **8** Greek character, police officer, last person to abuse (3-7)
- **11** Pressman's only one right person in divorce case (2-10)
- **14** Immature adult hands out foreign coin (10)
- **17** Take up imposing position on theme-park's top attraction (8)
- **19** Bird has single cocktail (7)

69

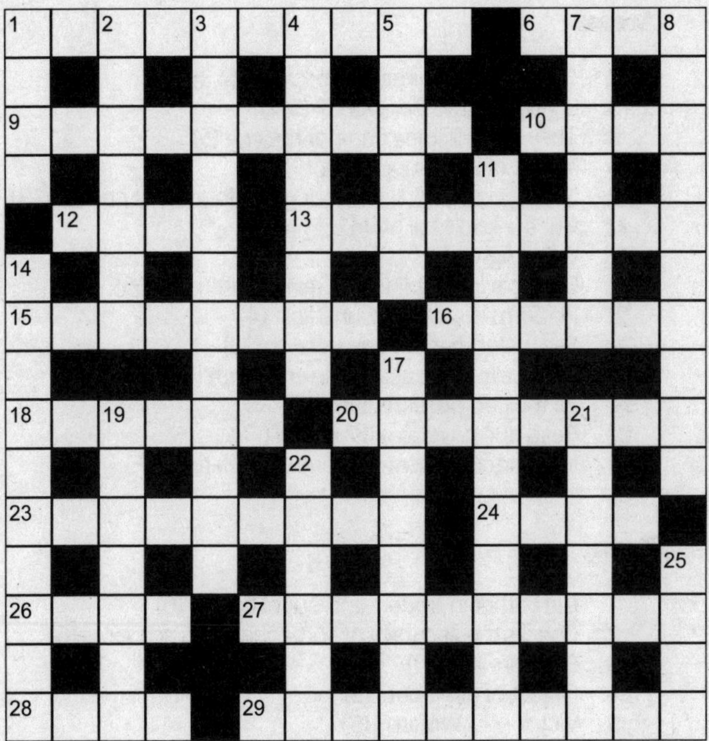

21 Enthusiast takes a friend to ancient city (7)
22 Wrote in confinement (6)
25 Rouse gentleman — about time (4)

Across

1 Confirm wild animal has escaped (4,3)
5 Big shot in the film world? (5-2)
9 They meet in the centre of the ring (5)
10 A host of local supporters (9)
11 Losing a point at tennis but going for runs at cricket (7,3)
12 Cut the bird's tail off (4)
14 Catch fighting? (4,8)
18 Bring back discipline and revive fraternity (7,5)
21 Platform is said to be unstable (4)
22 Sea water that's in one's watch (10)
25 Unusually fierce sea battle ends with it (9)
26 All the composer required (5)
27 Read one novel in girls' school (7)
28 It contracts to continue one's circulation (7)

Down

1 Girl bather in trouble and out of breath (6)
2 Checks the accuracy of someone else's accounts (6)
3 First former? (10)
4 Object of night out? (5)
5 Victor – or William? (9)
6 Finished in government (4)
7 Could be next Open champion, perhaps (8)
8 Go into liquidation when working hard (8)
13 They manipulate people to their advantage (10)
15 Height of architectural front? (9)
16 Radio executive sets up record (8)
17 Guess I'm in property (8)
19 Writer has way to tuck in inside French restaurant (6)
20 Fire when an explosive's not set? (6)
23 The more of them one has, the more one wants (5)
24 Two notes to measure (4)

70

70

Across

1 He coaxes reluctant dancer to writhe about with her holding arm (5,7)
9 Bury's features shared link (9)
10 Bohemian bar being talked about (5)
11 Small loans to young people (3-3)
12 Forsaken beauty loses cool (8)
13 US raid 'compromised' – that's the line coming from centre (6)
15 Refute *Sun*'s in favour of stopping deception in football (8)
18 Hysterical F-Frenchman's habitual response (8)
19 With 40% cutback analyst is one with target to hit (6)
21 Sedate umpire's ringing 'Caught!' (8)
23 Recommend healthy yodelling to help musical beginners when beat (6)
26 Some Abba wannabes backing Prince (5)
27 Redesign a core site for specialist publications (9)
28 Impression of something about to happen here – people are gripped by it (12)

Down

1 Rocky feints with right slug (7)
2 Temperature on high following air-conditioning malfunction (3,2)
3 Transport EU partner fixed (9)
4 Some macho axe-wielding fool (4)
5 Rebellious chorister lacking special eloquence (8)
6 Compère, familiarly, seems clever off and on (5)
7 The mob he organised is something enormous (8)
8 Modest husband belonging to exclusive social class (6)
14 Sea's blue inherently (4,4)
16 Board game is cheaper version (9)
17 Lethargic and lacking an agenda? (8)
18 Kindle typeface accommodates Middle English (6)

20 Balance affected manner with righteous heart (7)
22 Brace bendy pole (5)
24 Sudden pain expelling start of gastric wind (5)
25 Gosh, Beethoven's Ninth is old-fashioned stuff (4)

Across

1 Damn the two of them, getting European allowance (11)
9 Social climber's winning way, and skill (7)
10 One of four children aboard liner forming teams (6)
12 Quickly run out by a league member (7)
13 Carry on suits an eccentric (7)
14 Measures of energy in sleep (5)
15 Fleet docked with sick old animal (9)
17 Instrument for strategic planner around house (9)
20 The outskirts of Chester in view from loose rocks on hill (5)
22 Broken-down old mare's elevated position (7)
24 First-class average set back after a medical condition (7)
25 Bottle full of soup oddly in sight (6)
26 Mainly unlisted mobile device (7)
27 Tory tempters falling out in argument (11)

Down

2 Fruit mountains after the first of October (7)
3 Tricky problem – damaged tooth needs a crown put back in (3,6)
4 Head of school involved in knocks and scrapes (5)
5 Faith expressed in being tied up (7)
6 Eccentric's love doubled outside dance (7)
7 Rule leaves volatile fund managers in trouble? (3,3,5)
8 Trees concealing small book (6)
11 Not reliable at work and insufferable (11)
16 Painting adult touring fashionable island (9)
18 Wine firm providing cover for Independent series of columns (7)
19 Agree on ring but altered, without question (2,5)
20 Disturb son, out of bed, eating fish (5,2)
21 Unmarried woman supporting soldiers gets careless (6)
23 Trace elements surrounding rising general confusion (5)

72

72

Across

1 Pirate's earthy character for the audience (7)
5 Lady of the French game (7)
9 Parading topless with a bow? (7)
10 Woolf in essence shows skill (7)
11 Ecdysiast ends in act showing little bust (9)
12 Stop terrorist head backing state (5)
13 Clown, often melancholy, improvising caricatures initially? (5)
15 Canon with dire changes for sacrament (9)
17 Poor signs perhaps for medical forecast (9)
19 Indian capital (5)
22 Beam's, say, providing lift (5)
23 Enclosure crammed keeping Queen band together (2-7)
25 Sweetheart with reason to get touchy (7)
26 New Avenger giving chase (7)
27 Policeman's discharge around large parade (7)
28 Hill's divided by rushing stream (7)

Down

1 Traditional Catholic in charge of controlling girl (7)
2 Redeem seeing miracle play (7)
3 Nice parting speech? (5)
4 Just ego's hurt I fancy (9)
5 Writer gave up on Old English (5)
6 Tin or can possibly holding last of preserve? (9)
7 Oriental bird after endless happiness (7)
8 Little friendship following second love (7)
14 Incorrigible, wasting time relaxing (9)
16 Shady girl flashed on street (9)
17 Warn of downfall supporting left (7)
18 Threatening nothing less, accepting nothing (7)
20 Win over a team leader in position (7)
21 Fire was one thing to heat water (7)

23 Tough chop found in empty carvery (5)
24 Uplifting piano music by the French composer (5)

Across

7 One group wants attendant around to provide guidance (8)
9 General as fellow going after blood, no end (6)
10 Some duffer mathematically? Yes and no! (6)
11 Wicked king's army destroyed sultan (8)
12 Magnificent residence with fantastic ambience a help, including lake (8,6)
15 Injury requires member to be seen by hospital (4)
17 Fielders making mistakes (5)
19 Bird — young cat gets the tail of one (4)
20 Diversion that could put the sewer temporarily out of action (4,3,7)
23 Rare boat fashioned from various woods specially cultivated (8)
25 Dormant a short time in period before Easter (6)
27 Design of trendy shelter (6)
28 'Left on ship' is about right! (8)

Down

1 Religious tome's heartless anger (4)
2 Person with little time for Cornish town (6)
3 Attack making one hide (4)
4 Business programme in information carried by a US lawyer (6)
5 Bird featured in what is dull lecture for listeners (5,3)
6 Finish with copper getting mad, giving description of written evidence (10)
8 Performer in a cape with long hair (7)
13 Thrashing could make hate linger (10)
14 State with sea to east (5)
16 Fellows embarrassed, about to get counselled (8)
18 Theologian perhaps affected by the sun when going outside church (7)

74

21 Go short on food – nice things like chocolates? (6)
22 Poet's change of posture (6)
24 Supporter is silly guy losing head (4)
26 Agent may have hurried up when getting cold (4)

Across

1 Have forty-one winks? (9)
9 Type of selling still has first-class backing (7)
10 Expand measure by stirring lager (7)
11 Trouble taking drug? One's likely to complain (7)
12 Commonplace parking requires licence (9)
14 African moving nearer to snare it (8)
15 It is made to scale (6)
17 See slip being adjusted in coat (7)
20 Window decoration keeps out unknown missile (6)
23 Sudanese variety entertainer (8)
25 Only chap on strike? (3,3,3)
26 Nothing at breakfast that will make porridge? (7)
27 Member's turn to compose form of delivery (3,4)
28 Cash register silver deposited by Earl for cultivation (7)
29 Scented drink could be got up stream perhaps (9)

Down

2 Article in house that adds taste (7)
3 Baked a Dorset recipe (7)
4 Four-fifths of regulation twisted cord (8)
5 Take a little from top and bottom of loaf, getting put in dock (6)
6 Barker embarrassed over yours truly (3,6)
7 One does not continue giving a plug (7)
8 Exclude offer from local worker (9)
13 Determined to have detectives involved in act (7)
15 One boasting gaudy entrance (9)
16 Short-lived hybrid of maple here (9)
18 Beastly rush (8)
19 Set up in booth (7)
21 One cannot remember having it (7)
22 Learned European wants hors d'oeuvres topped and tailed (7)

24 You need to get over replacing a tray (6)

Across

1 Leaped — above oneself? (6,2)
6 Cut it and keep quiet (6)
9 Two men cut down prey (6)
10 Evocative of European river ebbing fast (8)
11 Knots of painters? (8)
12 She and men get involved and become engaged (6)
13 Speed check (12)
16 Holy orders? (12)
19 Doesn't fancy being under the influence (6)
21 Anticipate warning shout to Gessler's opponent (8)
23 One gets fed up with people (8)
24 Result in changes for part of Ireland (6)
25 Many dwell on this anagram made by setter (6)
26 Bought back, having had second thoughts? (8)

Down

2 International group is performing in concert (6)
3 Floral decoration in plate manufacture (5)
4 Party dress container found in good order (9)
5 Reading *Country Girl* (7)
6 Beg for keys (5)
7 They spend their time together (4-5)
8 It's not a close-up, you can bet on it (4,4)
13 Funny comedian touring North, in total control (9)
14 Make a series of calls on zero zero (4,5)
15 Agree to get less (8)
17 It will give you warmth and peace (7)
18 Uncover swindle (6)
20 Financial obligation limits university entrance (5)
22 Discrimination 23 Across appreciates in people (5)

76

Across

7 Status seeker on horseback, in front of jump (7)
9 Eccentric back with university, the French count (7)
10 Ram a truck's rear wheels and this may be broken (5)
11 Completely at a disadvantage, the Conservatives (9)
12 Chief administrator, noted career girl in resort (8-7)
13 Saw rambler in pub, disheartened (7)
16 Resume painting after nap (7)
19 Hurry to one at Skegness, rearranged (3,4,6,2)
23 Fashionable boy's name, reportedly? Seriously (2,7)
24 True male domain (5)
25 Ride a bike, holding on in tropical storm (7)
26 Channel Islands firm demonstrating a tank (7)

Down

1 Duly pick out fair game? (5,3)
2 Page item, tiny piece (8)
3 Academic ignoring American in workroom (6)
4 Customer apt to dither? Right on! (6)
5 Country record includes live song (8)
6 Clubs, later, reformed syndicate (6)
8 Excellent management, but lacking foresight (5)
9 Wealthy old lady's flutter after function (7)
14 Go beyond social welfare? (8)
15 Beset with bees bumbling around one, say (7)
17 Cook, perhaps, posed with flag on roof of theatre (8)
18 Number Ten upset about empty emporium, large building in Scotland? (8)
19 Light out around Cape causes a sudden problem (6)
20 Name weapon limited in scope (6)
21 Tackle school producing tasteless art (6)
22 Reprimand son towards the end (5)

77

Across

1 Showing caution about church's aggressive slogan (3,3)
4 A vessel welcomes test, oddly, but doesn't behave right (4,2)
8 Doctor looks sulky, accommodating old hippies (8)
10 Bank on road taking odds not often seen (6)
11 Happy clearing — finishing early (4)
12 Explosive assertion about daughter's skill (10)
13 The freedom of Paris? (5,7)
16 Drag one in? The first shall be last (5-7)
20 Bet impression includes church forerunner (10)
21 Affectation shown by topless couples (4)
22 A divine being in Father's place of worship (6)
23 Speculator's tense — gold pinched in robbery (8)
24 Left without cover, and fair worn out (6)
25 Take some diplomat on a launch without a key (6)

Down

1 Look drawn out with no new things to be done (8)
2 Quick foray, seizing power (5)
3 Pointed remark suppressed by sources in Radio Hallam and University is nonsense (7)
5 Joker gets one bill to do with heart (7)
6 Writer on board for runners (9)
7 European buff (6)
9 Program for organising broadcast, needing cover (11)
14 Reprimanded by annoyed American (6,3)
15 Repairs carried out before the end of April in revenge (8)
17 Finished a case of Camembert and ham (7)
18 Back down and negotiate in support of engineers (7)
19 Rile poor Argentine with no time at home (6)
21 Media pronouncement covering what to wear (5)

78

Across

7 Monkey revealing part of body among second group (8)
9 Satisfying English number getting disgusted reaction (6)
10 Provide service for heavy object, we hear (4)
11 Eastern fighter with restricted allowance for going abroad (10)
12 Appropriate feature in snooker? (6)
14 One taking a dip grabbing note for rest (8)
15 Figure recalled greed, perhaps, in sport (6)
17 Record created by me in sea in France? (6)
20 Beverage about to be consumed by fellow, getting half each (5,3)
22 Effect of quake seen in backward capital? Right (6)
23 Seize for use a new group of animals after taking firm measure (10)
24 Immense French novelist almost close to irreplaceable (4)
25 Major route and place providing setting (6)
26 Legal body overturning core of matter in hearing (8)

Down

1 Idle figure and aggressive youth hanging around a tree on the way up (8)
2 Rude remarks amid stress muttered (4)
3 Face venomous creature needing specialist treatment (6)
4 Salesman, one in endless celebration, getting suspension (8)
5 Jogger to step into ground (4-2,4)
6 Pass by topless Italian ladies (6)
8 Strain to acquire one pound for headwear (6)
13 Woman helping to accommodate Danes? (10)
16 Latin bus crashed in foreign city (8)
18 Port manufactured great armour, perhaps (4,4)
19 Clear head needed by conservationists (6)
21 Man on board that is inexperienced type (6)

22 Retire with last instalment of pension in Italian city (4,2)
24 Quantity of fish in dining area reported (4)

Across

5 Reproach worker maybe when protecting scoundrel (6)
8 Nasty b-bit of meat cast into pit (8)
9 Strong fellow, a joke at first (7)
10 Fellow with no money at all needing a change of direction (5)
11 A hope that may go up in smoke? (4,5)
13 A drug, fixed amount? It may provide fizz (8)
14 A lot of lies from children meeting teacher initially? (6)
17 Cook fish early on (3)
19 The fellow touching maiden where the skirt ends (3)
20 Artist in restaurant gets less than a whole bottle of wine? (6)
23 Norm accompanies one Welsh girl in a foreign capital (8)
26 Mused, being sent back (9)
28 Man of words I understand mostly, given time (5)
29 Is copper tucking into portion that can be eaten? (7)
30 Example set by weird ancients (8)
31 Salt that ruins dosage (3,3)

Down

1 Quiet house facing endless prejudice and fear (6)
2 A right problematical situation when there's nothing in wardrobe (7)
3 'Stupid boy' will be brought before teachers, that's very plain (9)
4 Drink disgusting pop in Syrian city (6)
5 She's not fair catch, nabbed by cruel person (8)
6 Bishop spanning many years becomes angry person (5)
7 Wicked king beat voluntary soldiers and left country briefly (8)
12 Where to drink at home — end of garden (3)
15 I am getting on to motorway grid to move to new territory (9)

80

16 Low-minded policy that limits play at Wimbledon (8)
18 Coming to and feeling the pain come back? (8)
21 Copy making up bulk of paper (3)
22 Evil drink may lead to good chanting (7)
24 A depression very briefly set in? It suggests Christmas is coming! (6)
25 Requirement to keep dry and secure in fishing boat? (6)
27 Intelligible and not completely ridiculous on reflection (5)

Across

1 Tune *Let it Be* with score showing extremes of emotion (15)
9 Suitor turning to a girl possessing sex appeal (9)
10 Minor player in film score (not a hit) (5)
11 It's glorious heading off in the past (5)
12 Department's holding two-thirds of red glandular product (9)
13 Ridiculous one like that in Irish city (8)
14 Mean to finish one set of books first (6)
16 Bring into use from French tactic (6)
18 Staid set affected repugnance (8)
22 Step in fat that's spread widely (6,3)
23 It'll secure entrance in flat cheaply (5)
24 German agreement on port wine (5)
25 Hymn from Southern religious ceremony (9)
26 Ah stinger sneaks — could be this! (5,2,3,5)

Down

1 Engineer allowed to overturn car (7)
2 Ring performer — stick at amateur set up (7)
3 Sporting grandpa goes once in childish event (3-3-5,4)
4 Stalwart is trying to show great skill (8)
5 Idle perhaps keeping new husband to provide fortune (6)
6 It's impossible to predict as votes are not being counted (6,2,7)
7 Can learn it in new way (7)
8 Had strong desire to restore deanery (7)
15 Assembly with wealthy old film star (8)
16 Places with little vegetation or leaves (7)
17 A piece of wood salesman erected as garden feature (7)
19 Served up an essential in the form of fruit (7)
20 Former lover taking hard drinks expires (7)
21 Detective held by hired thug — a protégé of Corleone? (6)

81

Across

1 Possibly one's private abomination (3,8)
9 Angostura put out for Jason's crew (9)
10 Fights for the best theatre seats (5)
11 A song from Iolanthe, maybe (6)
12 Understood devil came to a lawful end (8)
13 Raises new taxes, accepting pound (6)
15 New star dies in Act of God, perhaps (8)
18 Regular lay preachers take this (8)
19 Averts shambles – fast! (6)
21 Denial of victim in valid case (8)
23 I'm given role to communicate (6)
26 The result of a summer's work? (5)
27 A spirited community? Surely not! (5,4)
28 Version of carol *Silent Night* is heard (3,8)

Down

1 Calm sort of current in South American river (7)
2 Fast affected by drink? (5)
3 Rows of houses to sell on state order (9)
4 It scatters the foe right away (4)
5 In such a state there's no need for alarm (8)
6 This prize elevates the good in French language (5)
7 Someone calling for a mask – that's about it (7)
8 Dead estate agent (8)
14 Create novel about graduate in distress (8)
16 Yet someone has to pull the trigger (9)
17 Cut short acrimony – compromise (8)
18 Singular mistake in Latin translation (7)
20 Dead to the world (7)
22 Inclines to be quixotic? (5)
24 As you can see, it forms a ring (5)
25 The first person on a Scottish isle (4)

82

1		2		3		4		5		6				7
												8		
9										10				
11							12							
13		14					15			16				
						17								
18									19					20
21				22					23			24		
								25						
26						27								
				28										

Across

1 What chef prepares food on duty? The best! (7)
5 Travelled on horse, by the sound of it, with Member of Parliament holding a route finder? (4,3)
9 Ascetic possessing cold nature (7)
10 Typical ancient city in old African province (7)
11 Bully's mistake — wearing crooked ties (9)
12 Strike a mate (5)
13 Conclusion about this compiler's correct (5)
15 Spinning, thin pike caught not initially in perfect condition (2,3,4)
17 Needing support of French writer, having depression (9)
19 Some task I'm prepared to economise (5)
22 Plague remedy includes sulphur (5)
23 All at sea like tar — on this? (3,6)
25 Rock tour in US without hit, finally getting wrecked (7)
26 Fatty apes do start to ignore bananas (7)
27 Beware of group's fixed attitude (7)
28 Intellectual urge by school principal (7)

Down

1 Women are dancing the twist (7)
2 Extra something inaccurate tennis player might do? (7)
3 Dance beat with energy (5)
4 Sheer drop in cost is epic, possibly (9)
5 Gran cooked on English stove (5)
6 Those who criticise fancy cakes and tart (9)
7 Swallow one drink (7)
8 People regularly want fish (7)
14 Party held to annoy American? Risky (9)
16 Bird's poorly — took food to stimulate (9)
17 Colour scheme by mummy oddly ignored good taste (7)
18 Left on ship with one working part (7)

83

20 Bogarde, perhaps, missing first part? Tedious (7)
21 Don crept out, ignoring BBC's last forecast (7)
23 Genesis on television (5)
24 Copying recording but missing start (5)

Across

1 Without a taxi back, gets something to eat (5)
4 Cook's part played by fool in church (9)
9 Question put to cleaner: 'What would chef do?' (9)
10 Carpenter's key joints (5)
11 Sweet abandon, embracing sin (not at home) (7)
12 Area of ship producing the best team? (7)
13 Lost shirt? Time and drink will cure it (6)
15 Dish for preparing oakum to protect area on ship (8)
18 Daughters heartlessly surrounding a fashionable couple to get treats (8)
20 Scoundrel's terrible horse, say, full of energy (3,3)
23 Tea with fresh pita bread (7)
24 Hopeful, as Agnes reveals what's for dinner (7)
26 Dwell on origin of oak tree (5)
27 New deal with China providing food for Mexico (9)
28 Thoughtful friend with no name for food cooked so (4-5)
29 Ray's small girl in musical (5)

Down

1 Defender, old-fashioned but effective in retrospect (4-5)
2 Credit sailors for things caught at sea (5)
3 Raising weapon, acquires some bits of gold (7)
4 Material from tip in Czech Republic (6)
5 Clue for 'Liquid' requires it! (8)
6 Gets away from rest inside, with carbon copies (7)
7 Independent spirit stifled by talk, but begin (9)
8 Result in French – institute legal proceedings (5)
14 I married one, a vet – it turns out to be not the real thing (9)
16 Total attendance after George gets in terrible rage (9)
17 Sickness of one supporting kid in ale (4-4)
19 Thief's contribution to hot drink (3,4)
21 Comes down and lies around after six-pack (7)

84

22 Head of clan wears tartan, unruffled (6)
23 My editor talked lovingly! (5)
25 Nation in the grip of thorough anarchy (5)

The Telegraph

Across

1 Spring's madness ends in bursts (6)
5 Staggering, naff flashy jewellery (8)
9 Nude crones cavorting for adults only? (10)
10 Bad habit's very cool (4)
11 Female left male lover carrying a torch (8)
12 Get another round in! (6)
13 Mythological figure seeing reflection? (4)
15 'Rock' perhaps, a drug (8)
18 General accepting medal for regular? (8)
19 Look nasty, we hear (4)
21 Pound's confining small animals (6)
23 Back in profit, I repaired to get drink (8)
25 *Express* and *Sun* showing arrogance (4)
26 Turning red, I entered, taking part (10)
27 Topping menu with orgies, not so bad (8)
28 Look concerned with pain returning (6)

Down

2 Sheet that's turned over for the French siesta (5)
3 Ship's mate's abnormal love in club (9)
4 Scarfs remains after last of leftovers (6)
5 Area of real danger, but I'm dubious (7,8)
6 Cool Queen, second time around (8)
7 Position going up and down (5)
8 Fruit centre in a confection (9)
14 Get up following terribly acute burn (9)
16 Left sweetheart first wearing wedding band (9)
17 Fantastic 'Pulp' in chorus (8)
20 Try again? (6)
22 Starters of seaweed, uncooked seafood's hidden inside (5)
24 Bull almost decapitated champion (5)

85

Across

1 Timid about a B&B that's dirty? (6)
4 This writer's wanting agreement to make impression (6)
8 Outside old university see awful rabble making attack (8)
10 Blemish of Greek character – that's about tax primarily? (6)
11 Rasp in row (4)
12 Troubled soul? Obtain forgiveness (10)
13 What could be statement in Holy Writ (3,9)
16 Traveller's joy? Senior citizen experiences it as hairy (3,4,5)
20 A comic Frenchman in group is to abandon principles (10)
21 List of chaps attending university (4)
22 This writer that is penning article, an unkind type (6)
23 French refusal to accept a European dictator (8)
24 Before start of ritual saint must be clothed in proper cloth (6)
25 Impassioned founder of cosmetics firm, foremost in toiletry (6)

Down

1 Special policemen releasing several imprisoned characters for example (8)
2 Leader of academy donated a plant (5)
3 Black donkey seen around British isle with a whole lot of plants and animals (7)
5 Wine's second retail outlet running short (7)
6 Great thinker, exceptional sort with tale to engage one (9)
7 Sort of girl that's grave with zero yen (6)
9 Star out in the distance followed by Scot who has dreadlocks? (11)
14 Numbers in the old days you would get on beach (9)
15 Institute's period of time for accommodating call (5,3)
17 Terrific marksman that sees nothing? (7)
18 No. 5 for Leeds, one who cries as a player on the field? (7)

19 Unhappy about page and about facing pages (6)
21 Yours truly's penning brief line as children's author (5)

Across

3 Everyday fare served up in exotic plates by parliament (6,4)
8 Tony goes mad about company magnate (6)
9 Included hug before first of dates (8)
10 Philip and Edward have to stop talking (4,4)
11 Partly rewrites the record book (6)
12 Footballer from batting team got out (6,4)
14 Appointing group of church workers during Advent (13)
20 Proposing sex not allowed round home (10)
22 It's a tricky problem if this vegetable is hot (6)
23 Seat in church not finished (8)
24 American misbehaves behind closed doors (2,6)
25 Dismiss article – this issue's volcanic (6)
26 After preparing tea, TV's dead – heartbroken! (10)

Down

1 Stirring icy gin, he should get clean (8)
2 Cleo's new ideology reveals grammatical flaw (8)
3 Bridge partners mentioned river siesta (6)
4 Last word in steam engines (4)
5 Left one with Bert struggling to find the words (8)
6 Hundreds on planet in want (6)
7 Time when cricketers might appear? (6)
13 Course of salts (5)
15 Popular without little bit of money? That's naive (8)
16 At that place drinks initially will be on the rocks (2,3,3)
17 Produce infusion of green tea (8)
18 Penny put on weight in spring (6)
19 Prohibit an Australian fruit (6)
21 Caught – but scored? (6)
23 Shy actors (4)

87

87

Across

1 Got key cut (7)
5 Drew the card out (7)
9 Two officers get together with a drink (5)
10 Firm can set out to restrict debt (9)
11 A succession of small bloomers (5,5)
12 Appears as laid back, but is on watch (4)
14 They recommend its men to sail abroad (12)
18 Receive satisfaction from supply to Longleat? (4,1,5,2)
21 Bread from trolley (4)
22 It's cold in the country – you need a fur (10)
25 Put in for one stripe during manoeuvres (9)
26 GP yet to be reappointed to African country (5)
27 Most women have this combination of give and take (7)
28 Wanted to see knight in action (7)

Down

1 Walton's deceptive appearance? (6)
2 Transposing the bookmaker's sign language is part of the strategy (6)
3 Lead, say, in hard rock (5,5)
4 The last place to fight? (5)
5 Proved to be a full member of the church (9)
6 They go round in circles (4)
7 Hot work during Test that contains century (8)
8 Reveal record to be unsuccessful (8)
13 Teaches a number limited by English, perhaps (10)
15 A piece of light music? (5,4)
16 A swimmer has first to get changed (8)
17 Sort of key that may be found in a cupboard? (8)
19 Musician puts sheet on piano? On the contrary (6)
20 Separated and left (6)
23 Donne has been translated quite a lot (2,3)
24 Short game in which a child goes to sleep (4)

88

88

Across

7 A beignet, say, may be healthier, doctor finally admitted (7)
8 A mostly forthright party delivering fruit (7)
10 Elected pope is harsh (9)
11 Record broken by unknown composer (5)
12 A well-bred fellow envoy (5)
13 Heels were broken in some other place (9)
15 Daughter is to perform on parade (7)
17 Ambassador briefly produces certificate (7)
18 Trouble during first half of reel after square dance (9)
20 Touchy about conductor's first musical arrangement (5)
21 Gather mother's upset by idiot (5)
23 Lack of faith shown by Delibes, I suspect, before start of fugue (9)
24 Expunction comes with time, certainly (7)
25 Many G and Ts poured out in tumbler (7)

Down

1 East Sussex town's victory over London club (10)
2 Bowled, during a trial, under the most favourable conditions (2,4)
3 Leaves writer lines (8)
4 Chapter on law imposed on American plant (6)
5 Subsequent examination of dog at an end (6-2)
6 Fish, black when small (4)
7 Honest description of old-fashioned blonde? (4-3-6)
9 Where the clock's hands are, as is palpably plain (2,3,4,2,2)
14 Prudent, comic alone in resort (10)
16 Songbird seen on branch line flower (8)
17 Event for equestrian in period costume, primarily (8)
19 Large snake may make one run (6)
20 Sordid around Turkey's capital, like the baths there? (6)
22 A short talk by Greek hero (4)

89

89

Across

1 Jessica, on computer game at Olympics ... (5,6)
9 ... to confront elite, gets personal application (4,5)
10 Short quarter-sections enclosed (5)
11 Fake reporting of school tests by heads of English and religion (6)
12 Boring tools for American lawyer in messy fights (8)
13 Gets rid of clothes for theatre (6)
15 Question and answer in front of school lines (8)
18 Key expert, except on odds (5,3)
19 Stops going by car when holidays are mentioned (6)
21 Where strikers are seen to fight after game? (8)
23 Cause devastation, writing a volume in anger (6)
26 American in Jamaica jailing assassin (5)
27 Picture file misplaced by alcohol producer (5,4)
28 Fifty for cooked lunch after journey's end (4-7)

Down

1 Start to think of charges for sweets (7)
2 Resists responsibilities? (5)
3 Celibate pinching kiss getting worked-up and emotional (9)
4 Regular revenue (with no regret) (4)
5 Lots of euros lost supporting miners (8)
6 Harshly criticised missing student, having had enough (5)
7 A relative newcomer walks forward? (7)
8 Disadvantage of retreat? (8)
14 Convert rags into carpeting (8)
16 Sailor chap wearing waterproof (9)
17 Song about America and wild partying (8)
18 Groundbreaking work of menials? (7)
20 Background for part of play on track (7)
22 The Prime Minister to have meals in hotels? (5)
24 So long a day — that is the 2nd of July (5)

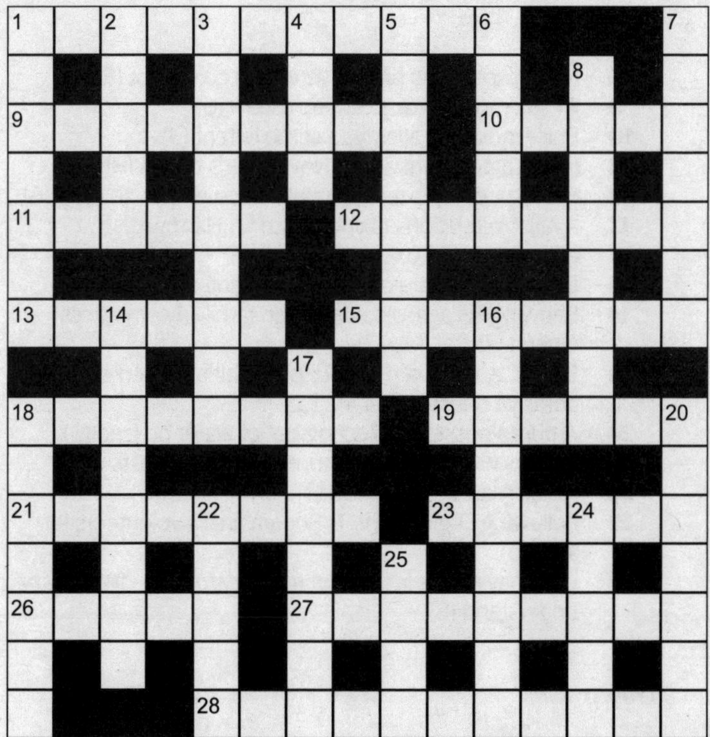

25 One's often slipped making a record (4)

Across

8 Newspaper boss backed intended contempt (8)
9 At sea most of cargo enters astern (6)
10 Pulse indicated allergy to some extent (3)
11 Not in agreement about November's bonus (8)
12 First pair of reporters favourite to cover area in *Echo* (6)
13 Available relations taking coach for Harrow or elsewhere (6-3,6)
15 Daughter's poor exam result bringing disgrace (7)
18 Showing his age, old comic Ken familiarly embraces Queen (7)
21 Be polite, be aware of your place initially, then employ abrasive questions (4,4,2,3,2)
24 A pump possibly collecting last of water on land (6)
25 Visitors who want to be superior to their hosts (4,4)
26 Horse manure's no good (3)
27 Following English runs, R. Bopara finally volunteers for slips (6)
28 Love having her little bit of money around — that's easy to understand (8)

Down

1 *Enigma* to be broadcast — I will knock out a sign (6)
2 First-class fish on the decline (6)
3 Penned acid needy letters about national celebration (12,3)
4 Beast's outspoken answer to 'Which wine, darling?' (3,4)
5 Two creatures sheltering hospital cat turning up in overhanging growth (6,9)
6 To lose one's footing wearing boots perhaps is careless (8)
7 Gush about a jam lover (8)
14 Find fault with hack (3)
16 Delegate with messy air, disorientated (8)
17 Hancock character — one with expression of disappointment — in funny drama (5,3)

91

19 Aim to get goal (3)
20 Obliquely question expert about the capital of Norway (7)
22 Lack of volunteers to join railway – official (6)
23 Mini designer holds Issigonis's original – it's charmingly old-fashioned (6)

Across

1 Dramatist taking care of orphan maybe after Christmas (4,6)
6 Unwanted message quietly received by pianist in film (4)
9 As we rather suspect, it's a bird (10)
10 Restriction – Father Christmas's helpers reduced by half (4)
12 Christmas cards? Mum has one left (4)
13 Those growing up eat greens with difficulty (9)
15 Santa is often here going about (2,3,3)
16 Season of snow – interminable? (6)
18 Good person facing danger – ultimately I have to try very hard (6)
20 Ship takes fellow beyond part of the Commonwealth (8)
23 Unsatisfactory – one church in which one has a limited time to perform ritual? (9)
24 Vegetables returning the end of this month (4)
26 A model hiding nothing? Such may be seen in church! (4)
27 I can sledge around, look, at an angle! (4,6)
28 It's said you will this festive tide (4)
29 Plodding that took couple to Bethlehem (6,4)

Down

1 Organ making din – one needs to escape (4)
2 Graceful flying angel entering from beyond our world (7)
3 Woman's hesitation over something wicked in seasonal act of worship (5,7)
4 Victory spanning the world to become less plausible? (4,4)
5 Old magistrates, very English, laid into Welshman? (6)
7 It's gratefully received here and now – dispatched in advance? (7)
8 Remote inns dished out soup (10)
11 Activity in which only some of the children are little angels (8,4)

92

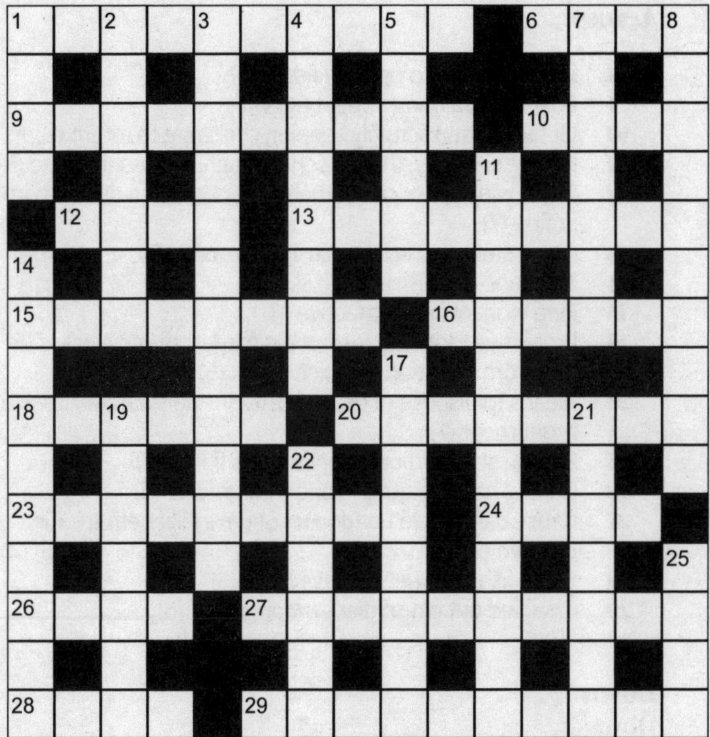

14 Evangelist is on Jerusalem's hill protected by mother at Christmas (10)
17 A joint response that lacks proper thought? (4-4)
19 Earfuls blasted to convey negative message (7)
21 Short note sent round hospital department as a reminder (7)
22 Unrefined stuff in musical I composed (6)
25 Wise Men had to — to observe King (4)

92

Across

1 Waste energy to operate fiddle (6)
4 Posh car following street buggy (8)
10 Outlaw posed scruffily keeping challenge to return (9)
11 Having celebrity, this person is caught in passing craze (5)
12 Right-wing American somehow reckoned to ditch Obama at first (7)
13 Cajun stew — one left pain in the mouth (7)
14 A section downsized with skill (5)
15 Fine work of art is attractive (8)
18 Protective footwear for work in garden after excesses (8)
20 Pick from selection a choice snack (5)
23 Means to dispose of dead mostly surrounded by massive monument (7)
25 Singing style let flow over listeners finally (7)
26 Central heating ailing — one may get this (5)
27 Cause damage to London museum's Elizabeth the First of England (9)
28 Snare fish after net damaged (8)
29 Checked out old soldier's unruly youth (6)

Down

1 Pretentious air actually existing among stars (8)
2 The rest live around university (7)
3 Feel anger towards being taken in by a frontman (9)
5 Admitting taking steps, knowing what one has in mind (7-7)
6 Charity needs steer over footballers with money (5)
7 A politician in mostly crazy satire (7)
8 Anger about theologian's tricky question (6)
9 Mention Nick ... here he comes! (4,2,3,5)
16 Passes fish agreement (9)
17 Protector of flock to collect old money keeping nothing (8)
19 Composer anticipates court decision (7)

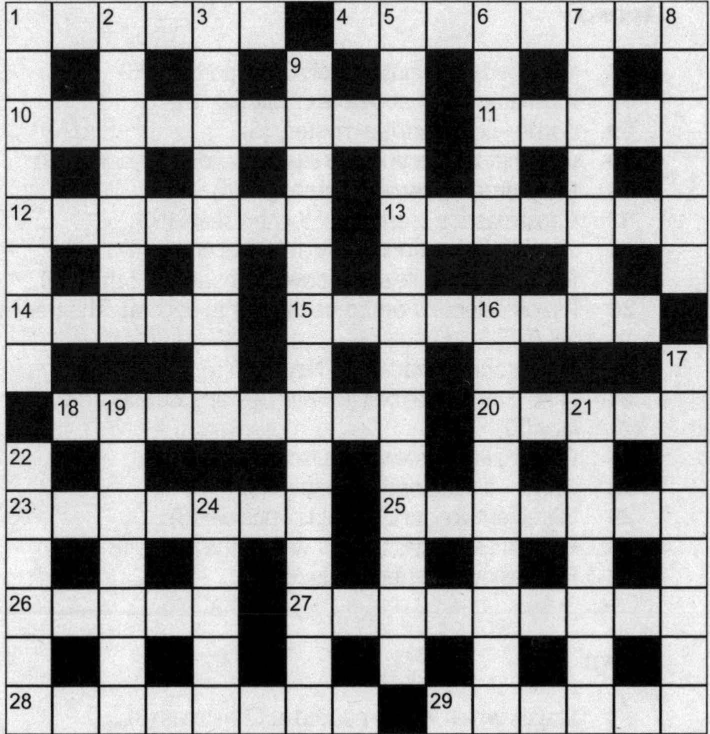

21 Talk going round Brazilian city in vehicle (7)
22 A cheap reconditioned helicopter (6)
24 Gibson perhaps willing to get fruit (5)

Across

1 Wrapped gift, being soft on Clare, perhaps (6)
4 It's suspended just before Christmas (8)
9 Game in crackers is a mystery (6)
10 One that talks one round to see Handel's *Messiah*? (8)
12 Dead drunk, providing old stories (4)
13 Christmastide presents of theatre seats (5)
14 Party includes a number in religious group (4)
17 Famous play in its second week on January 5th? (7,5)
20 Rip off celebrant out to be the first to decorate the tree in UK (6,6)
23 Pass around a traditional New Year's gift (4)
24 I had conducted the carollers, perhaps, but became lazy (5)
25 Christmas spirit always surrounds her (4)
28 Drink — it's the end of the bird (8)
29 Ingredients relating to cold mince pie (6)
30 Presents for ladies are out with some circles (8)
31 Fancies outsize tree inside (6)

Down

1 Stages which will be packed at Christmas (8)
2 They lead the way in the present transport system (8)
3 These trees may be obtained from Wilhelmstrasse (4)
5 They gave original Christmas presents (5,4,3)
6 Trim tree finally with attractive result (4)
7 Where Jesus lived is setting up a king (6)
8 About the end of December, reached Santa's base (6)
11 Like Idle Jack in pantomime? Definitely not (7,5)
15 By start of evening a Christmas tree may be lit up (5)
16 What may be decked, when sun rises, will (5)
18 Tiptoe in craftily to get round robin (8)
19 Run out of decorations in packets, perhaps (8)
21 Frozen hanger-on (6)

22 A Christmas present drawer (6)
26 It may hold needles on the tree – but only as a present (4)
27 Watch punch initially trickle away (4)

Across

1 Brown, for example, is strangely typical – a bit not quite all there (10)
6 Women chatter, with no time for ramble (4)
9 Lunch today for unfriendly old gaoler with no name? (4,6)
10 Road back north is a bore (4)
12 Medicine ball (4)
13 Felt awkward concerning small meal today? (9)
15 The effect of drinking gin, initially in a royal house? (8)
16 Reportedly grab a salad, of sorts (6)
18 A depression in case of locals getting grants (6)
20 It wears shades for callers (8)
23 The rest of the family is on alert, perhaps (9)
24 Finally, somebody to bring America exercises (4)
26 Most of monarchy blow their own trumpet (4)
27 Propose rank new material for board (5,5)
28 Look before getting cover for serious deficit (4)
29 Flats pay me in new arrangement as mine's light (6,4)

Down

1 Get ready to fire mate (4)
2 The back seat for one working in support of 12 (7)
3 Fighting talk? (6,2,4)
4 Daughter in Roller I ordered gets more overbearing (8)
5 Start, seeing ambassador grabbed by one from Eton, for example (3,3)
7 Extreme letters when chasing beer and flowers (7)
8 Book on bridge in part of London (5,5)
11 Drama putting off my tailor, with wages covering last of material (8,4)
14 Dramatic articles on Conservative in court case (10)
17 Break up little girl's answer (8)
19 Runs awkwardly for some ices, expending minimum amount of cash (7)

95

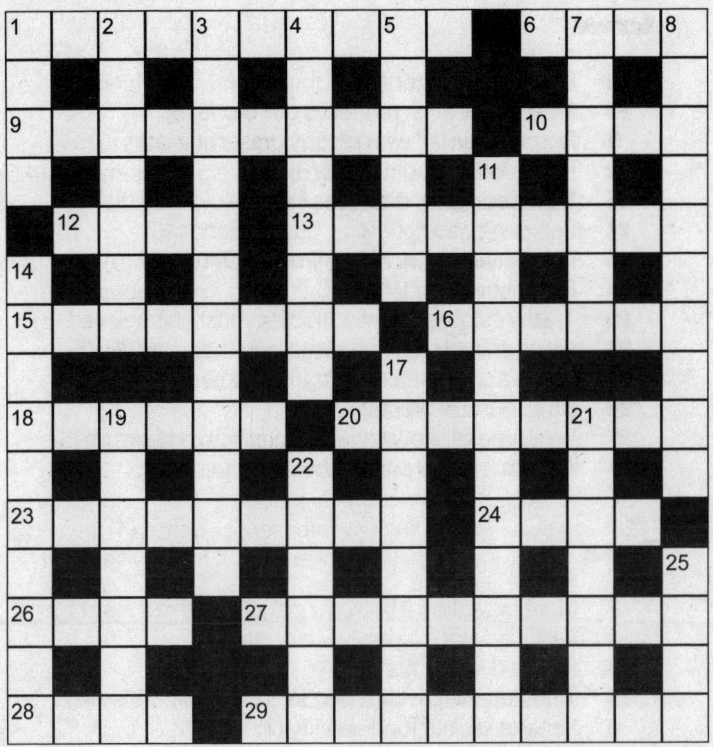

21 Material for soldiers nationalist's taken into Palestinian area (7)
22 Offspring attending a classical piece (6)
25 Break off due to exposure (4)

Across

1 Headlong plunge? (11)
10 Most of the drink produces dull drone (5)
11 Respectable ladies endlessly preserving jams (9)
12 Hands in a welcome deal (9)
13 Modelled your extremities for dirty old man (5)
14 Following good publicity, buy appliance (6)
16 Pot contains recipe before call of dinner (8)
18 Bum shown squashed (8)
20 Trashy establishment admitting most shamefaced (6)
23 Living animal reaching virtual adulthood initially (5)
24 Name a shrew rejected, start to tame shrew (9)
26 Drug found in property? (9)
27 Welcome to show lower regions with nothing on (5)
28 Act pains me to pieces covering Queen (11)

Down

2 More exceptional bottom upended without resistance (5)
3 Rival's advance to embrace darling (7)
4 Right's dead in dust (6)
5 Titles' opening with scoundrels Del and Rodney (8)
6 Senator sacked for disloyalty (7)
7 Left in fights, hurts a broken hand (8,5)
8 Repentant criminal with form getting time inside (8)
9 Garage patrons' toilet in need of facelift (6,7)
15 Funding raised over family abuse (8)
17 One's served in jug perhaps (8)
19 Vision of cat after face includes his head (7)
21 Pagan ardour on top of bird (7)
22 Gives someone the low-down underpants (6)
25 Dispense with amateur tax returns (5)

96

Across

7 Management of river in Norfolk town adjoining a lake (8)
9 Bird arrives diving into grass (6)
10 Scoundrel, in the course of time, makes mistakes (6)
11 Soldier receiving notice in a pickle (8)
12 Nutter in pother bungled car manoeuvre (5-5,4)
15 Harvest to get hold of round end of September (4)
17 English residing in opulent German state (5)
19 King articulate but no leader (4)
20 Family team was behind a fund for restoration (7,3,4)
23 Help one to get better for special type of race (8)
25 Expresses love when restricted by bad habits (6)
27 To wander round losing daughter is more despicable (6)
28 Hurried, always getting worried about it (8)

Down

1 Support lord audibly (4)
2 At university time for the latest news (6)
3 Criticise success that comes through lots of tricks (4)
4 Dissolute priest I found lacking energy and enthusiasm (6)
5 Calm knight leading queen into path (8)
6 False idol of French clan brandished in game (6,4)
8 Run away from snaky character, one who finds fault (7)
13 Unsentimental, as a boxer taking some punches needs to be? (4-6)
14 Poem I set down with a twist in it (5)
16 Writer has article about a sorrowful American city (8)
18 Linger outside an industrial city in Germany (7)
21 Short financial statement — something that may bind agreement (6)
22 Person in cafe — one has got soaked apparently! (6)
24 Group of Scouts prepare for camp? (4)
26 One is not fair (4)

97

The Telegraph

Across

8 Things drifting, not turned round by board (8)
9 In reception (2-4)
10 Agile Romeo embraced by Mata Hari? (4)
11 Fancy divorcee at ground (10)
12 Horse, cob Ron tamed (6)
14 Not good-looking! (4-4)
15 Comment on late news? (7)
17 Plants in this place may conceal trap (7)
20 Cleaner's mother welcoming one's special appeal (8)
22 Discrimination shown by second divorcee one's married (6)
23 List of items turns Liberal off (4,2,4)
24 Cut to remove bird's tail (4)
25 Being virtuous, he acts out of character (6)
26 Teacher's account seen by the man as source of worry (8)

Down

1 Nonsense to applaud with role backfiring (8)
2 Just nothing left in New York (4)
3 Boss takes leader of industrialists round workroom (6)
4 Hammer on the door? (7)
5 Type of crack that's parting? (8)
6 Gossip in phone kiosk? (10)
7 Film mob I've roused (1-5)
13 Tailless tarantula is bothering botanist (10)
16 Situation vacant, no stamp required (4-4)
18 Georgia's portable lamp (8)
19 Flair giving Peter pain (7)
21 Hospital overlooks number for summit (6)
22 Witness woodcutter's up-and-down motion (6)
24 Close main line (4)

98

Across

1 Occasion some face with resolution (3,5,3)
9 Want a little snow? (9)
10 A party disgrace (5)
11 Party drinks may get nasty glares (6)
12 Mean to endure? (5,3)
13 Appear in the nude — not how skater is normally seen (6)
15 Time to celebrate a form of mahogany (8)
18 Girl to check returned calendars (8)
19 Horses shouldn't be; hounds may be (6)
21 Roman water-carrier (8)
23 US author stirred Mavis in composition about love (6)
26 As they grow up they grow down (5)
27 Save money for drinks dispenser at the party (9)
28 Strangely easy, yet errs in description of the past? (11)

Down

1 Settles for ten less in exchange (7)
2 Grown like this, it's an offence (5)
3 Please have a party! (9)
4 Parting party guests may take one for it (4)
5 Some weakening of the party spirit? (8)
6 Long for New Year ahead (5)
7 Where the butts of a party congregate? (7)
8 Measure appropriate for some Londoners (4-4)
14 Party drink is unusual hit (3,5)
16 In which all men are brothers? (9)
17 Dies of cold? (3,5)
18 A row about boy appearing in pantomime (7)
20 Entertains in low joints — right? (7)
22 Study may easily become so if neglected (5)
24 Golden retriever's mate? (5)
25 A bird engaged in making her nest (4)

99

99

Across

1 Go on about head of root vegetable (6)
5 Last, in spite of expectations to the contrary (5,3)
9 One qualified to make songs better? (6,2,5)
10 Good manners in palace? Yes, all over the place (8)
11 Favourite left out? That's brave (6)
12 Rumour about harbour (6)
14 Tread on someone's toes — each corn, unfortunately! (8)
16 Very strong players attached to golf club (4-4)
19 New weapon, limited in scope (6)
21 Suppress attacks backing the French (6)
23 Passionate games played by workers in shorts (3,5)
25 Reciprocal match in centre of Margate (13)
26 Warder releasing fine bird (3-5)
27 Horse, one of five in point-to-point? (6)

Down

2 Father rounding on innkeeper (7)
3 Code word used by radio's 'Caroline'? (5)
4 What could make row? Estate car, perhaps (9)
5 Assistant in a small company, reportedly not a heavyweight (7)
6 Pale, Italian climbing, lacking courage (5)
7 Ice, mostly, on top of old Irish lake (9)
8 Using few words, endlessly beat a prisoner inside (7)
13 Not properly adjusted, hence future too unpredictable (3,2,4)
15 Chapter on posture in *Lady Chatterley*, for example (9)
17 Piece in paper, tiny piece with no heading (7)
18 Rank outsider? Work on her jumping outside (2-5)
20 Ring about tie-on label on figure (7)
22 Incident in flat ending in arrest (5)
24 Farewell to the Parisian (5)

100

1	2		3		4		5		6		7		8	
	9													
10									11					
12			13				14		15					
16	17						18		19				20	
21					22		23				24			
	25													
26									27					

Solutions

Solutions 1–3

1

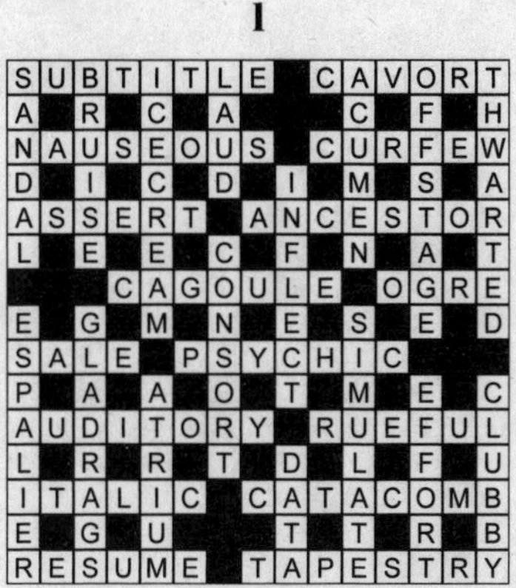

2

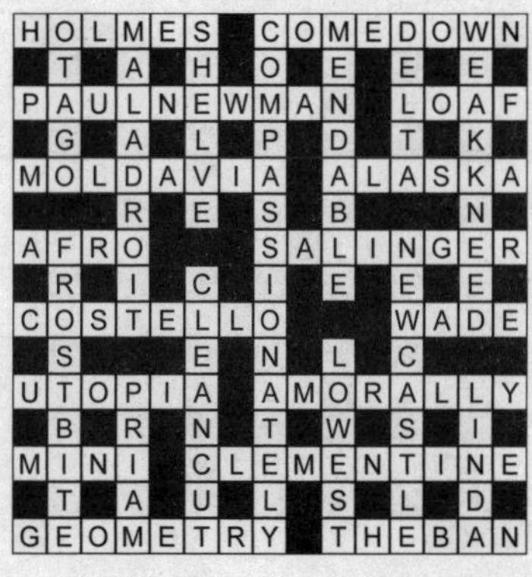

3

Solutions 4–6

4

P	R	O	B	A	B	I	L	I	T	Y				M
R		A		I		V		N		O		H		I
O	B	S	E	R	V	A	N	T		K	E	A	T	S
P		I		M		N		E		E		N		U
H	U	S	S	A	R		I	N	C	L	U	D	E	S
E				I				D				O		E
T	A	C	K	L	E		R	E	L	I	E	V	E	D
		R		E		F		D		N		E		
S	N	O	W	D	R	O	P		S	T	O	R	E	S
A		W				U				R				O
T	O	B	E	S	U	R	E		C	A	R	T	O	N
I		A		T		S		C		N		E		N
A	G	R	E	E		O	B	E	I	S	A	N	C	E
T		S		E		M		D		I		O		T
E				P	R	E	S	E	N	T	A	R	M	S

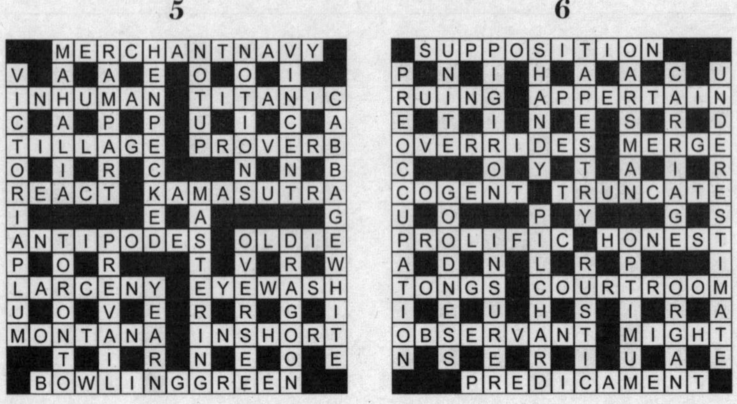

Solutions 7–9

7

8

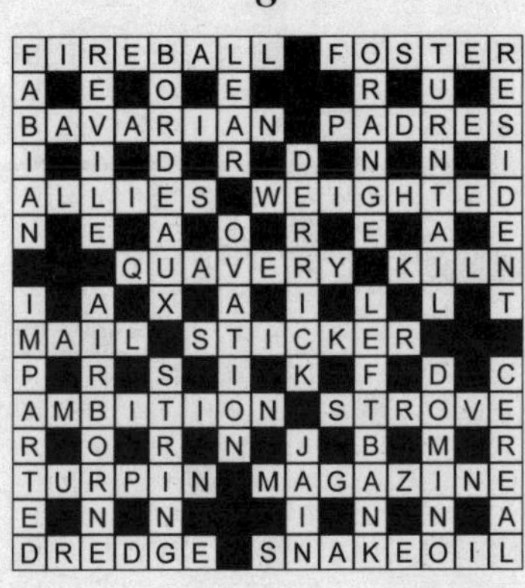

9

Solutions 10–12

10

11

	P	A	W	N	E	E		O	D	D	S	O	N	
	A		O		P				I		W		I	
C	R	O	N	Y	I	S	M		S	T	E	A	M	Y
	K		K		C		A		T		E		B	
C	L	O	Y		U	B	I	Q	U	I	T	O	U	S
	A				R		N		R		N		S	
U	N	A	C	C	E	P	T	A	B	L	E			
	E		H				E				S		O	
			I	N	C	O	N	C	L	U	S	I	V	E
	F		L		O		A		E				E	
N	E	G	L	I	G	E	N	C	E		F	U	R	L
	C		I		N		C		C		U		C	
T	U	N	D	R	A		E	T	H	E	R	E	A	L
	N		O		T				E		Z		S	
	D	O	G	L	E	G		A	S	P	E	C	T	

12

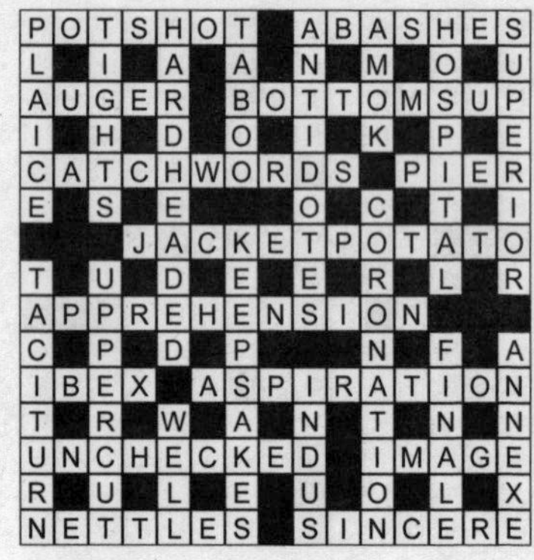

Solutions 13–15

13

14

15

LEVERAGE ICICLE
A A O O H L T
TINSMITH MOSAIC
E D U O L M E
SHALLOT SHERBET
T L U H U R A E
SLEEPWALKER
T B W E E A
WHEELBARROW
O N E L F E K G
FANTAIL ILLWILL
A E S C L G I
CAVEIN FIRSTAID
E I N A E L E
DESIGN CLOTHIER

Solutions 16–18

16

17

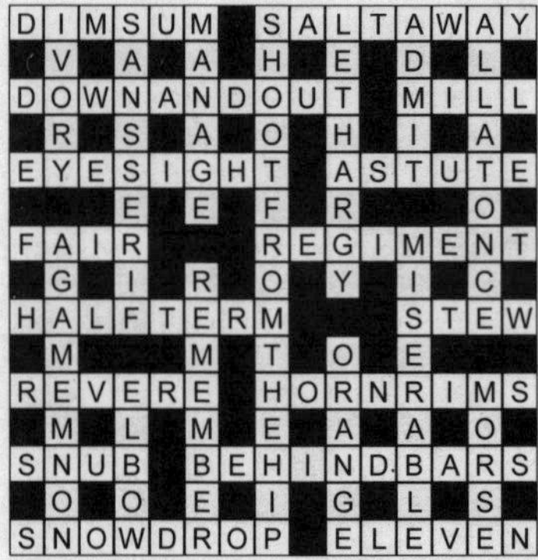

18

Solutions 19–21

19

20

21

Solutions 22–24

22

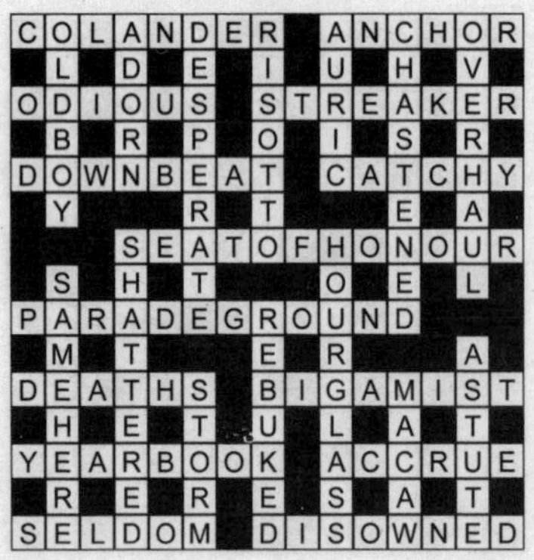

C	O	L	A	N	D	E	R	#	A	N	C	H	O	R
#	L	#	D	#	E	#	I	#	U	#	H	#	V	#
O	D	I	O	U	S	#	S	T	R	E	A	K	E	R
#	B	#	R	#	P	#	O	#	I	#	S	#	R	#
D	O	W	N	B	E	A	T	#	C	A	T	C	H	Y
#	Y	#	#	#	R	#	T	#	#	#	E	#	A	#
#	#	#	S	E	A	T	O	F	H	O	N	O	U	R
#	S	#	H	#	T	#	#	#	O	#	E	#	L	#
P	A	R	A	D	E	G	R	O	U	N	D	#	#	#
#	M	#	T	#	#	#	E	#	R	#	#	#	A	#
D	E	A	T	H	S	#	B	I	G	A	M	I	S	T
#	H	#	E	#	T	#	U	#	L	#	A	#	T	#
Y	E	A	R	B	O	O	K	#	A	C	C	R	U	E
#	R	#	E	#	R	#	E	#	S	#	A	#	T	#
S	E	L	D	O	M	#	D	I	S	O	W	N	E	D

23

K	E	I	T	H	#	P	L	A	I	N	T	I	F	F
N	#	N	#	A	#	R	#	N	#	I	#	N	#	A
I	N	C	U	M	B	E	N	T	#	G	A	U	D	I
F	#	U	#	B	#	F	#	E	#	G	#	N	#	N
E	A	R	L	O	B	E	#	R	E	A	L	I	S	T
E	#	#	#	N	#	R	#	O	#	R	#	F	#	#
D	A	M	P	E	R	#	W	O	N	D	R	O	U	S
G	#	A	#	#	#	N	#	M	#	#	#	R	#	U
E	Q	U	I	P	P	E	D	#	M	U	R	M	U	R
#	#	S	#	R	#	A	#	T	#	N	#	#	#	P
P	I	O	N	E	E	R	#	W	H	O	P	P	E	R
O	#	L	#	T	#	S	#	E	#	I	#	A	#	I
S	U	E	D	E	#	I	D	E	A	L	I	S	T	S
I	#	U	#	X	#	D	#	D	#	E	#	S	#	E
T	E	M	P	T	R	E	S	S	#	D	R	E	A	D

24

R	A	P	P	O	R	T	#	B	A	S	A	L	T	#
#	R	#	E	#	A	#	#	#	P	#	C	#	H	#
R	O	Y	A	L	I	S	T	#	P	I	Q	U	E	D
#	M	#	C	#	N	#	R	#	E	#	U	#	O	#
R	A	S	H	#	B	R	I	G	A	D	I	E	R	S
#	T	#	#	#	O	#	A	#	S	#	E	#	Y	#
R	I	G	H	T	W	I	N	G	E	R	S	#	#	#
#	C	#	I	#	#	#	G	#	#	#	C	#	B	#
#	#	#	S	U	B	C	U	T	A	N	E	O	U	S
#	P	#	T	#	E	#	L	#	N	#	#	#	L	#
C	L	E	A	N	S	L	A	T	E	#	L	O	L	L
#	I	#	M	#	I	#	T	#	R	#	E	#	E	#
V	A	R	I	E	D	#	E	N	O	R	M	I	T	Y
#	N	#	N	#	E	#	#	#	I	#	U	#	I	#
#	T	H	E	I	S	T	#	A	D	O	R	I	N	G

Solutions 25–27

25

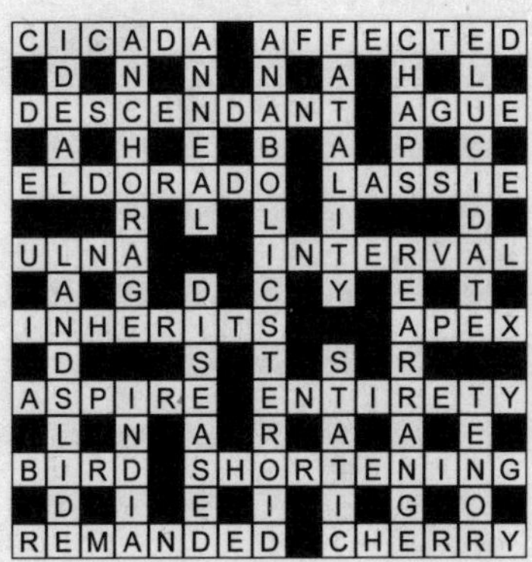

26

	S		S		B		C	O	N	T	R	A	C	T
H	E	C	U	B	A		I		E		U		A	
	N		N		N		N	I	C	K	N	A	M	E
S	E	L	F	M	A	D	E		K		I		P	
	G		L		N		M		W	I	N	T	E	R
P	A	N	O	R	A	M	A		E				R	
	L		W				T	R	A	V	E	R	S	E
			E		P		O		R		Y			
C	H	A	R	M	I	N	G				E		C	
	O				G		R	E	S	I	S	T	O	R
A	G	E	N	T	S		A		A		H		N	
	A		E		W		P	I	T	T	A	N	C	E
P	R	I	G	G	I	S	H		R		D		I	
	T		U		L		E		A	R	O	U	S	E
W	H	I	S	T	L	E	R		P		W		E	

27

Solutions 28–30

28

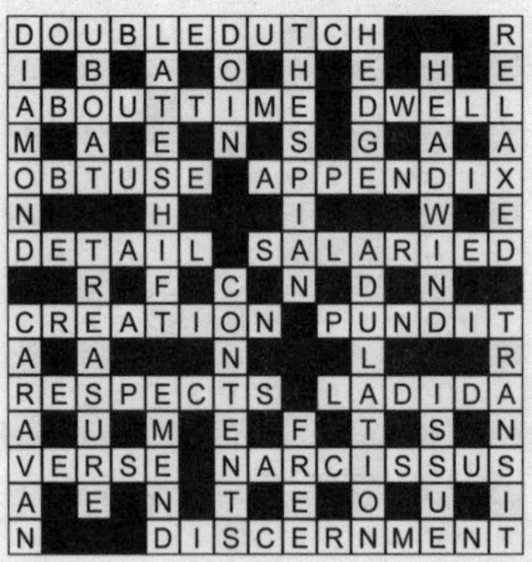

29

SCURRY VERBAL
O N E X I A
GLADRAGS CASINO
I E D U E H D
STAR IMPERSONAL
A E P P P U
TRAINSPOTTER
Y N S I P
STRAITJACKET
M I E T A N
MAIDMARIAN SACK
R E C O I A I
TOBOOT NOTATALL
O U O O A I
NATURE CRAYON

30

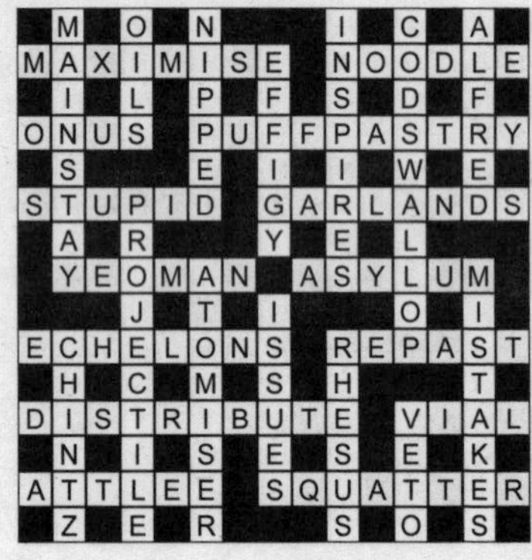

Solutions 31–33

31

G	O	N	E	W	I	T	H	T	H	E	W	I	N	D
R		E		I		R		E		N		M		E
A	T	T	E	N	T	I	O	N		T	I	A	R	A
T		B		D		A		A		E		G		R
I	S	A	A	C		N	O	N	E	N	T	I	T	Y
N		L		H		G		T		T		N		M
G	U	L	L	I	B	L	E		S	E	R	E	N	E
				L		E		M		C				
S	T	A	P	L	E		S	A	B	O	T	A	G	E
A		S		F		S		H		R		S		G
T	O	P	B	A	N	A	N	A		D	E	C	K	O
S		H		C		L		R		I		E		T
U	N	A	P	T		A	L	A	B	A	S	T	E	R
M		L		O		M		J		L		I		I
A	S	T	O	R	M	I	N	A	T	E	A	C	U	P

32

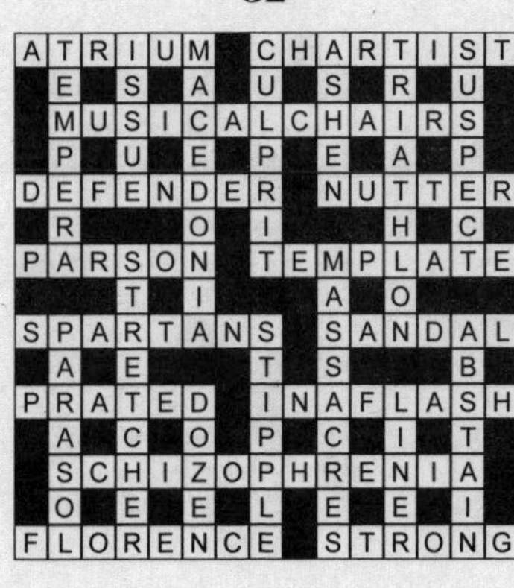

33

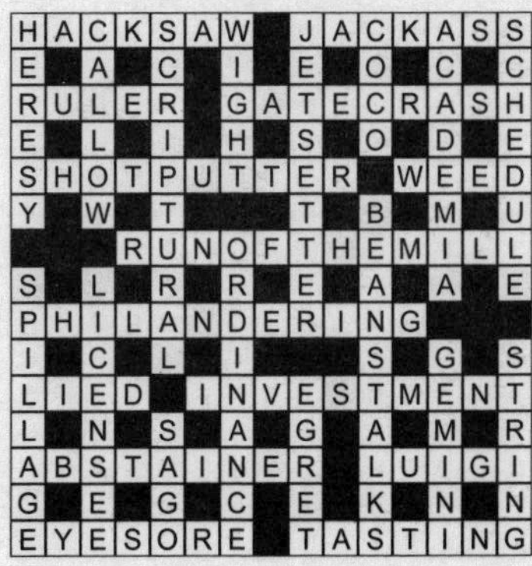

Solutions 34–36

34

35

W	O	R	S	H	I	P		D	E	C	L	A	R	E
E		E		A		E		R		O		R		L
A	N	G	R	I	E	R		I	G	N	O	R	E	D
L		U		R		F		V		D		A		E
T	E	L	E	S	C	O	P	E		I	N	N	E	R
H		A				R				T		G		L
Y	A	R	D	S		M	A	C	H	I	N	E	R	Y
				T		E		H		O				
C	O	M	M	A	N	D	E	R		N	E	R	V	E
H		E		N				I				E		N
A	W	A	R	D		A	S	S	E	M	B	L	E	D
I		S		A		T		T		U		E		L
N	E	U	T	R	A	L		M	E	S	S	A	G	E
E		R		D		A		A		E		S		S
D	R	E	S	S	E	S		S	A	D	N	E	S	S

36

Solutions 37–39

37

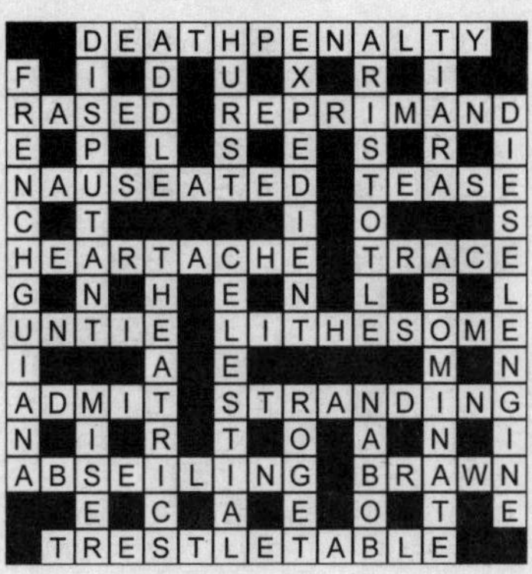

38

39

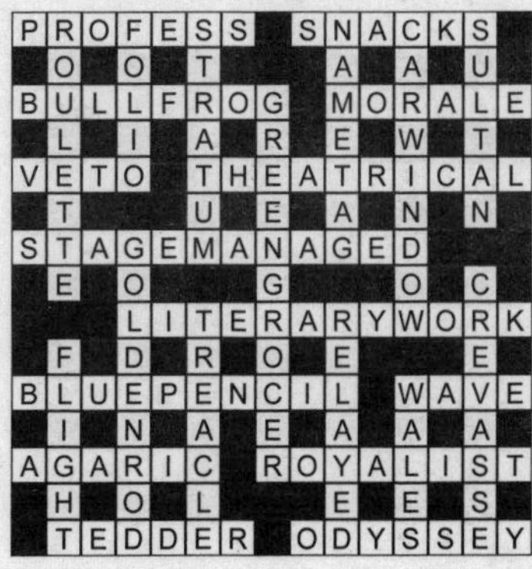

Solutions 40–42

40

41

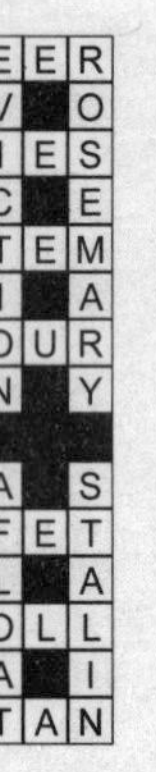

42

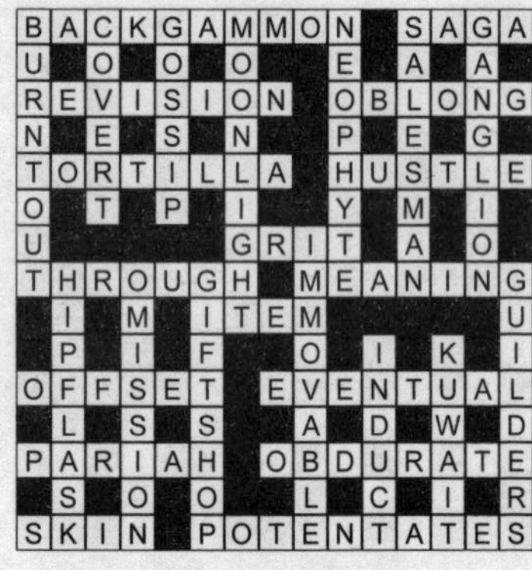

Solutions 43–45

43

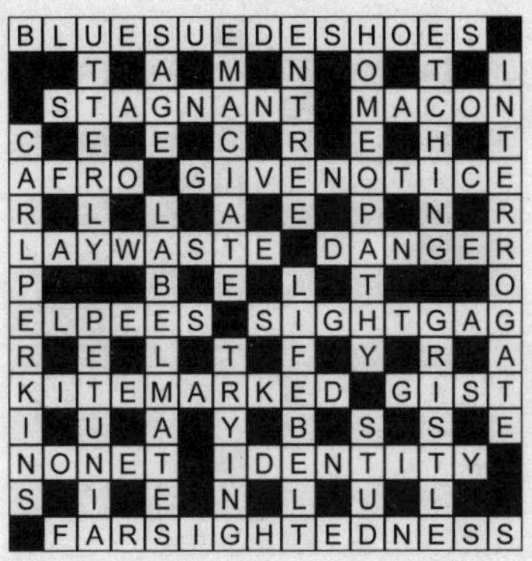

44

M	E	R	C	A	N	T	I	L	E		H	A	R	M
A		E		L		E		O				N		A
I	S	L	E	T		R	E	M	A	I	N	D	E	R
D		O		A		R		B		M		E		T
		C	O	R	S	I	C	A		P	A	S	T	E
F		A				E		R		A				N
O	C	T	O	B	E	R		D	I	L	A	T	E	S
R		E		L						A		R		I
G	O	S	P	O	R	T		D	E	S	C	A	N	T
E				T		R		E				V		E
A	D	U	L	T		A	D	V	E	R	S	E		
H		P		E		I		I		O		L		K
E	S	P	E	R	A	N	T	O		M	I	L	A	N
A		E				E		U		E		E		O
D	I	R	E		A	R	I	S	T	O	C	R	A	T

45

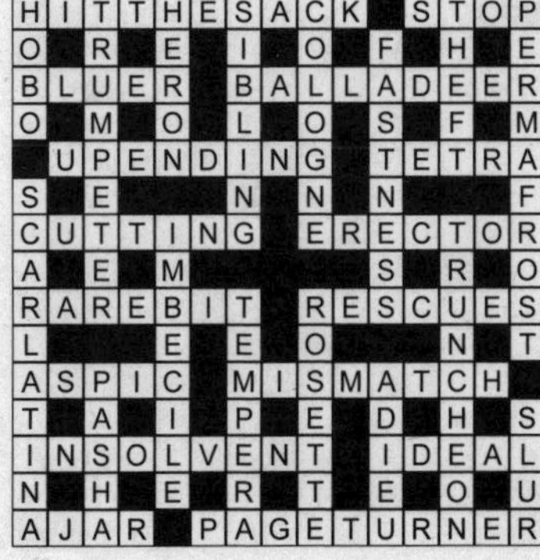

Solutions 46–48

46

47

48

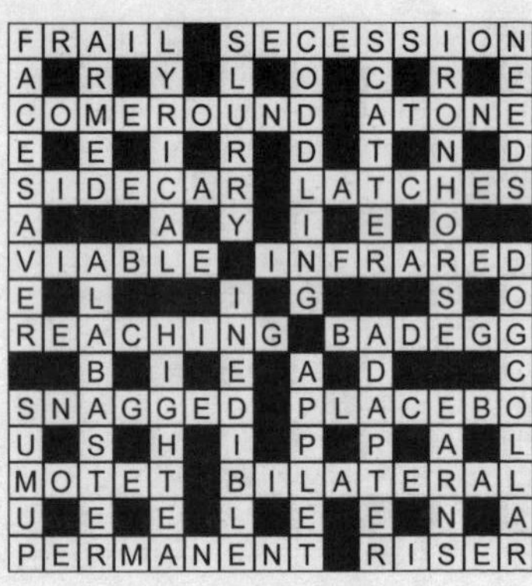

Solutions 49–51

49

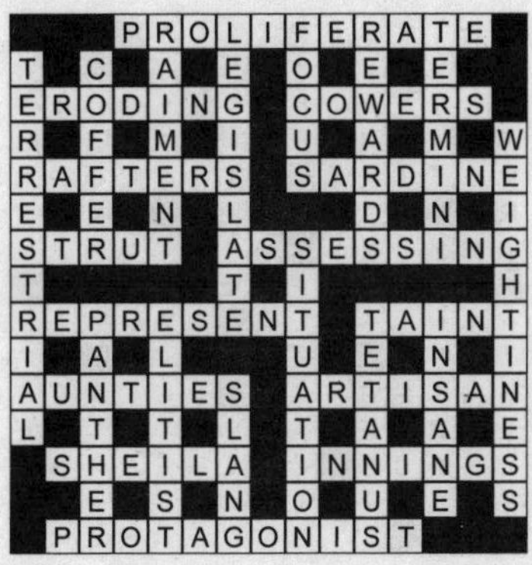

50

WRONGHEADED
I P R N E R
COLLATE DULLARD
O D Q E S I I I
NOCTURNE CRANKS
S A E P S I E A
TATA MANOEUVRER
E W R U M M
LAMBASTING AGHA
L I L Y D S R M
ARNOLD SPOILAGE
T I O B R T N N
ESCAPEE OUTCAST
A E E O E R
BIRDSOFPREY

51

Solutions 52–54

52

53

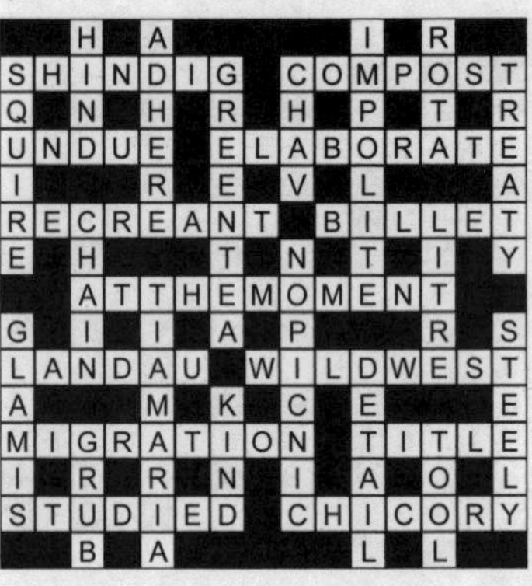

54

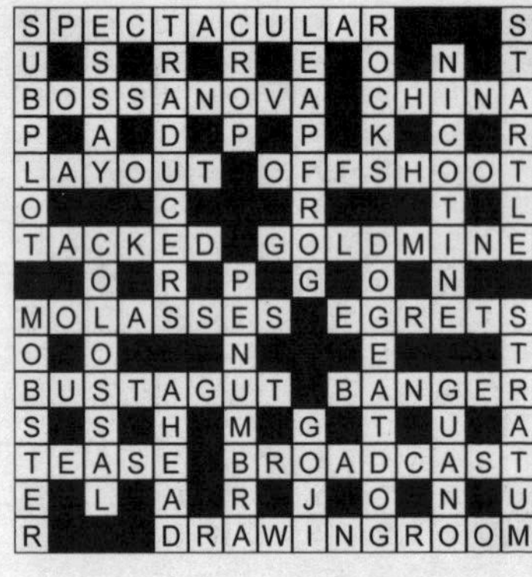

Solutions 55–57

55

56

T	H	R	E	A	D	B	A	R	E		K	I	E	V
E		E		S		L		E		T		L		I
C	A	D	E	T		A	L	C	O	H	O	L	I	C
H		A		H		C		A		I		I		A
I	N	C	H	E	C	K		P	A	R	T	N	E	R
E		T		C		M				D		O		A
			B	R	E	A	D	P	U	D	D	I	N	G
R		D		O		I		A		I		S		E
E	T	O	N	W	A	L	L	G	A	M	E			
M		G		F				E		E		F		F
E	N	G	U	L	F	S		T	A	N	G	I	E	R
M		E		I		E		H		S		S		I
B	A	R	K	E	E	P	E	R		I	N	C	A	S
E		E		S		I		E		O		A		K
R	O	L	E		P	A	T	E	R	N	A	L	L	Y

57

Solutions 58–60

58

59

60

Solutions 61–63

Solutions 64–66

64

65

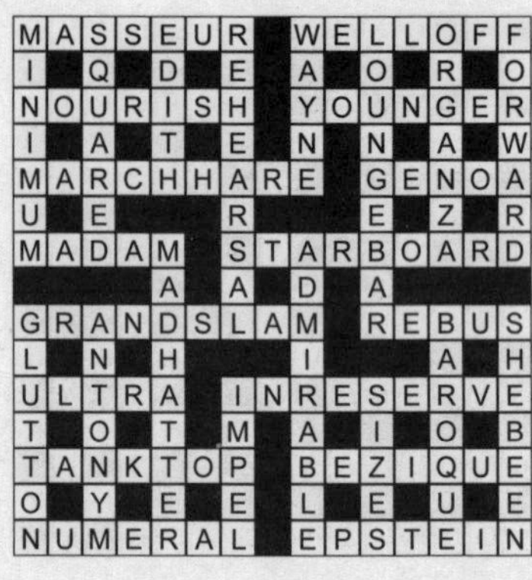

66

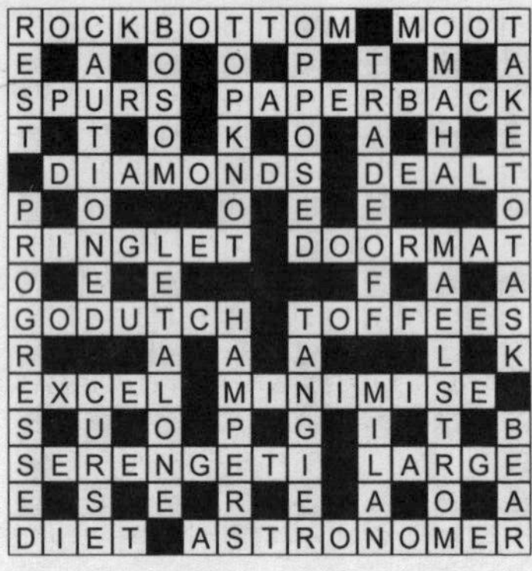

Solutions 67–69

67

68

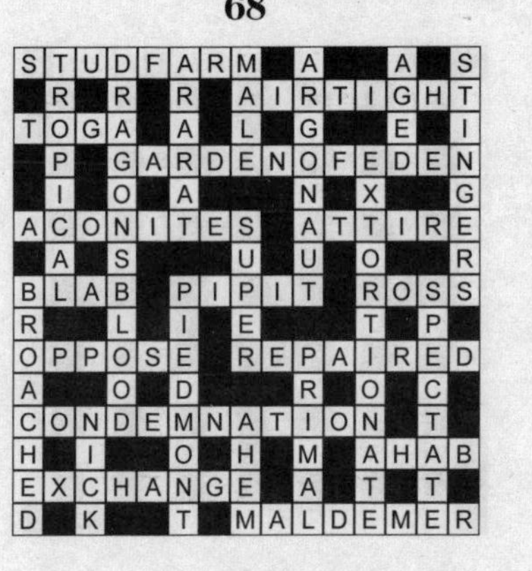

69

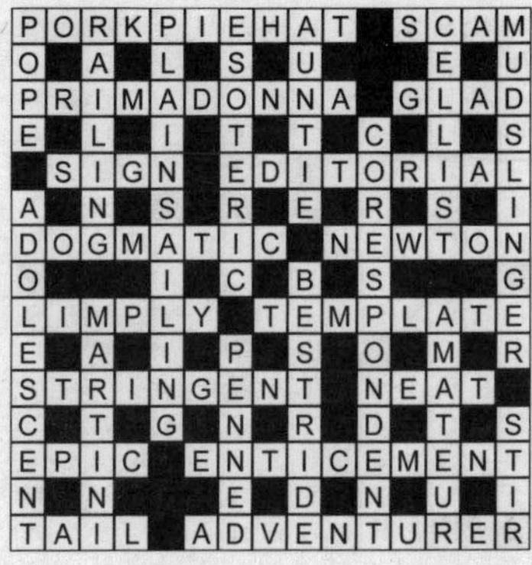

Solutions 70–72

70

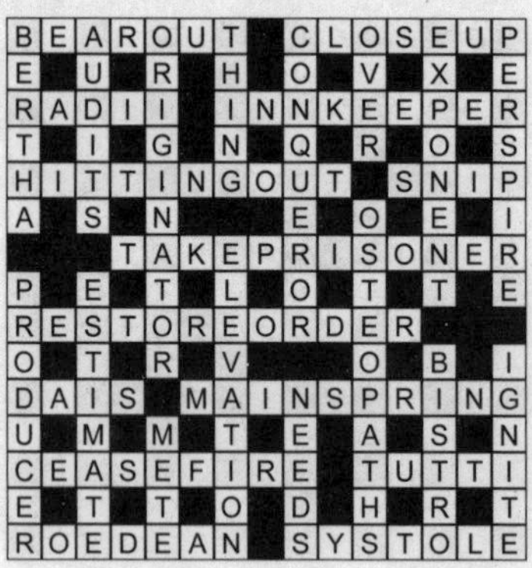

71

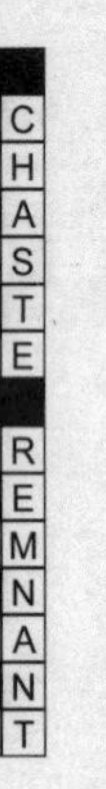

72

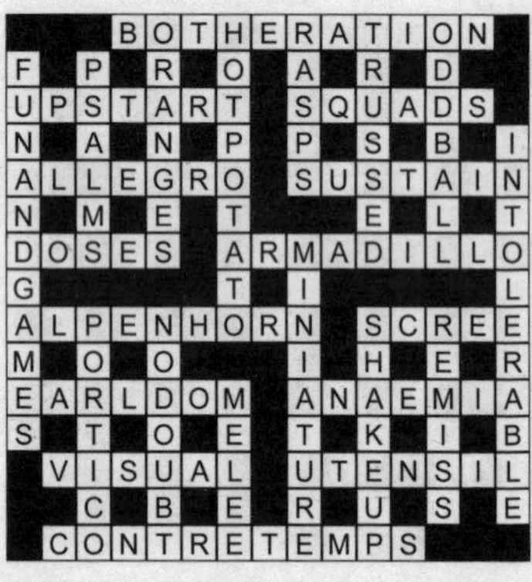

Solutions 73–75

73

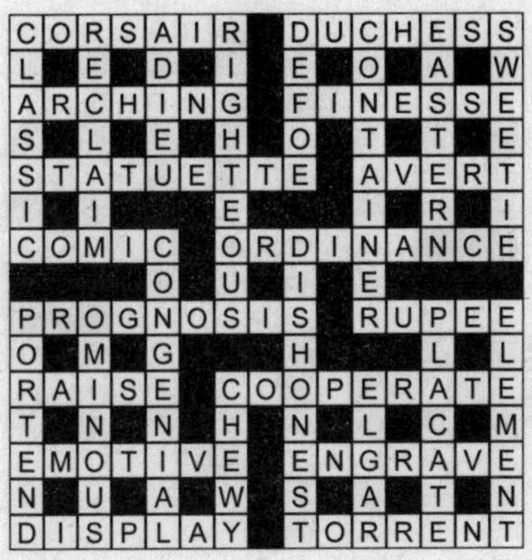

74

■	B	■	B	■	■	■	P	■	A	■	G	■	D	■
P	I	L	O	T	A	G	E	■	G	O	R	D	O	N
■	L	■	D	■	C	■	L	■	E	■	E	■	C	■
F	E	R	M	A	T	■	T	A	N	T	A	L	U	S
■	■	■	I	■	R	■	■	■	D	■	T	■	M	■
B	L	E	N	H	E	I	M	P	A	L	A	C	E	■
■	E	■	■	■	S	■	A	■	■	■	U	■	N	■
H	A	R	M	■	S	L	I	P	S	■	K	I	T	E
■	T	■	E	■	■	■	N	■	C	■	■	■	A	■
■	H	U	N	T	T	H	E	T	H	I	M	B	L	E
■	E	■	T	■	R	■	■	■	O	■	O	■	■	■
A	R	B	O	R	E	T	A	■	L	A	T	E	N	T
■	I	■	R	■	A	■	L	■	A	■	I	■	A	■
I	N	T	E	N	T	■	L	A	R	B	O	A	R	D
■	G	■	D	■	S	■	Y	■	■	■	N	■	C	■

75

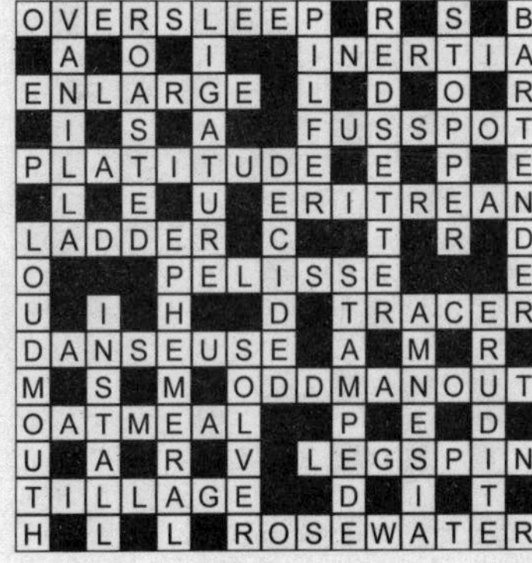

The Telegraph

Solutions 76–78

76

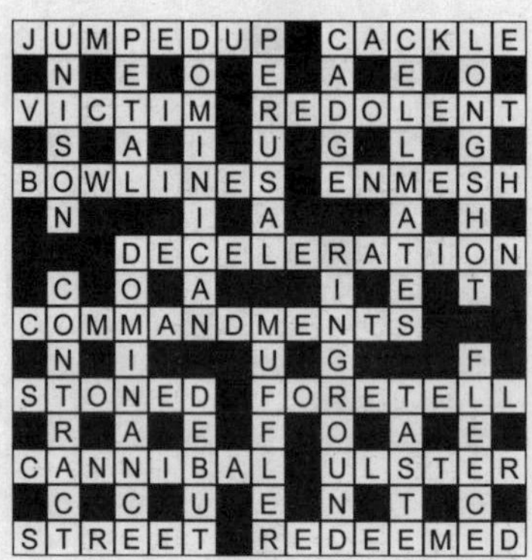

77

L				P		S				P		B		C
U	P	S	T	A	R	T		D	R	A	C	U	L	A
C		U		R		U		O		T		L		R
K	A	P	U	T		D	O	W	N	R	I	G	H	T
Y		E		I		I		A		O		A		E
D	I	R	E	C	T	O	R	G	E	N	E	R	A	L
I				L				E				I		
P	R	O	V	E	R	B		R	E	S	T	A	R	T
		U				E				A				E
G	E	T	O	N	E	S	S	K	A	T	E	S	O	N
L		R		A		I		I		I		L		E
I	N	E	A	R	N	E	S	T		R	E	A	L	M
T		A		R		G		S		I		T		E
C	Y	C	L	O	N	E		C	I	S	T	E	R	N
H		H		W				H		T				T

78

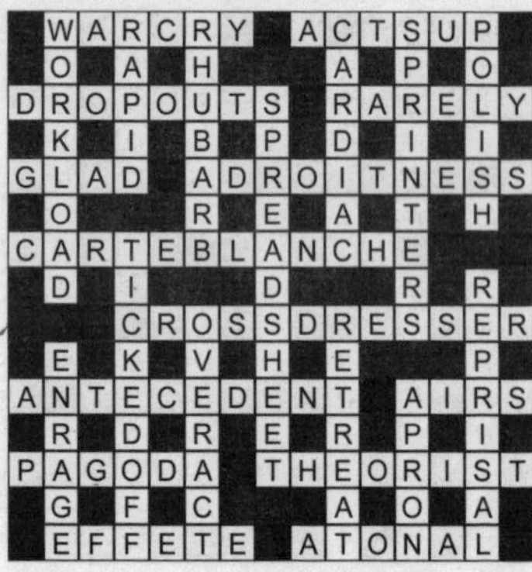

Solutions 79–81

79

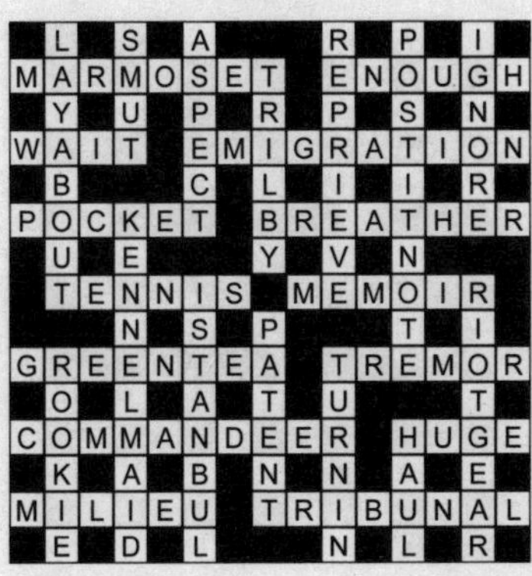

80

P		A		P		A			B	E	R	A	T	E
H	O	R	R	I	B	L	E		R		A		A	
O		M		K		E		P	U	N	G	E	N	T
B	L	O	K	E		P			N		E		T	
I		I		S		P	I	P	E	D	R	E	A	M
A	E	R	A	T	I	O	N		T				L	
		E		A			N		T	I	S	S	U	E
	B			F	R	Y		H	E	M			S	
C	A	R	A	F	E		A			M		S		
	S				A		P	A	R	I	S	I	A	N
R	E	F	L	E	C	T	E	D		G		N		E
	L		U		H			V		R	O	G	E	T
B	I	S	C	U	I	T		E		A		I		T
	N		I		N		I	N	S	T	A	N	C	E
S	E	A	D	O	G			T		E		G		D

81

Solutions 82–84

82

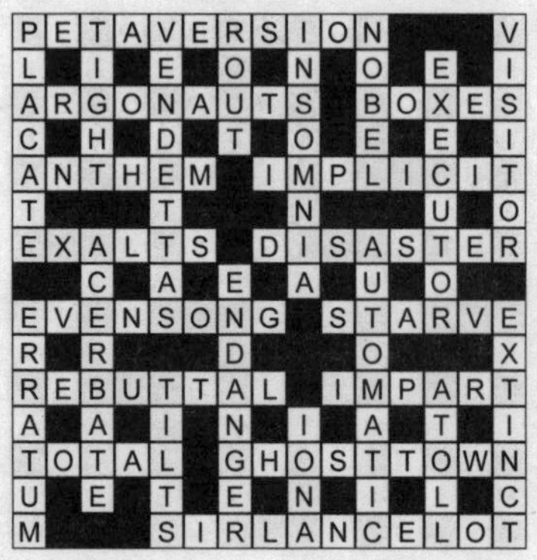

83

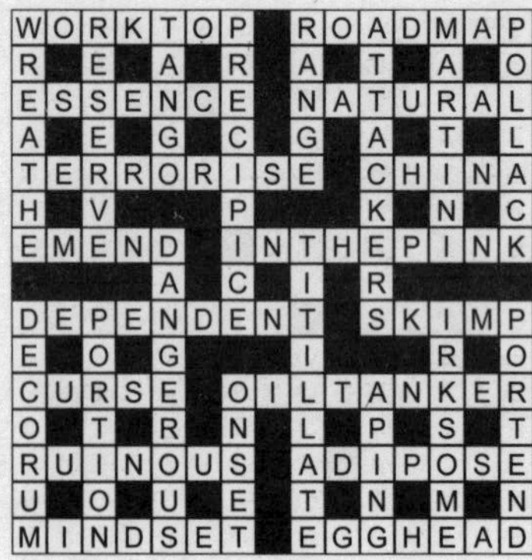

84

Solutions 85–87

85

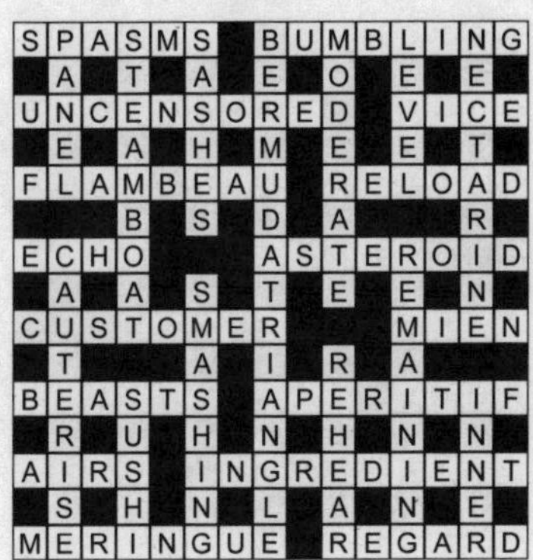

86

	S	H	A	B	B	Y		I	M	P	A	C	T	
	P		G		I				O		R		O	
B	E	L	A	B	O	U	R		S	T	I	G	M	A
	C		V		M		A		E		S		B	
F	I	L	E		A	B	S	O	L	U	T	I	O	N
	M				S		T		L		O		Y	
N	E	W	T	E	S	T	A	M	E	N	T			
	N		H				F				L		B	
			O	L	D	M	A	N	S	B	E	A	R	D
	S		U		E		R		W				I	
A	P	O	S	T	A	T	I	S	E		M	E	N	U
	R		A		D		A		E		I		G	
M	E	A	N	I	E		N	A	P	O	L	E	O	N
	A		D		Y				E		N		U	
	D	U	S	T	E	R		A	R	D	E	N	T	

87

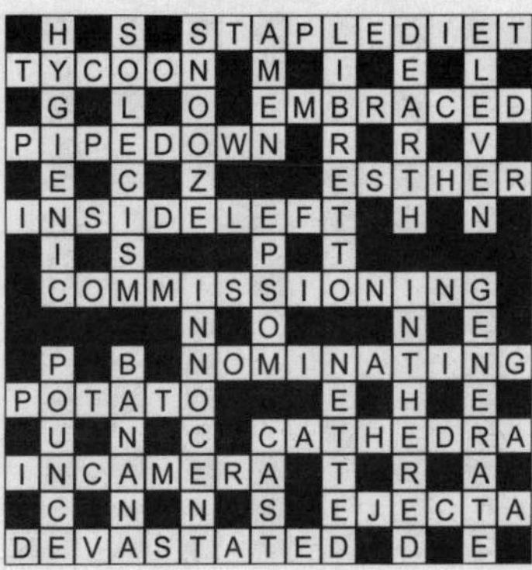

Solutions 88–90

88

89

		W		A		G		C		F		B		
F	R	I	T	T	E	R		A	V	O	C	A	D	O
A		N		B		E		C		L		S		N
I	N	C	L	E	M	E	N	T		L	I	S	Z	T
R		H		S		N		U		O				H
A	G	E	N	T		E	L	S	E	W	H	E	R	E
N		L				R				U		C		F
D	I	S	P	L	A	Y		D	I	P	L	O	M	A
S		E		A				R				N		C
Q	U	A	D	R	I	L	L	E		S	C	O	R	E
U				K		A		S		T		M		O
A	M	A	S	S		D	I	S	B	E	L	I	E	F
R		J		P		D		A		A		C		I
E	R	A	S	U	R	E		G	Y	M	N	A	S	T
		X		R		R		E		Y		L		

90

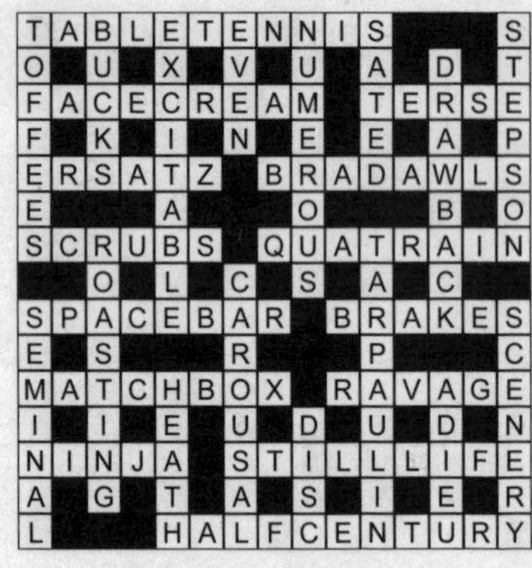

Solutions 91–93

91

92

93

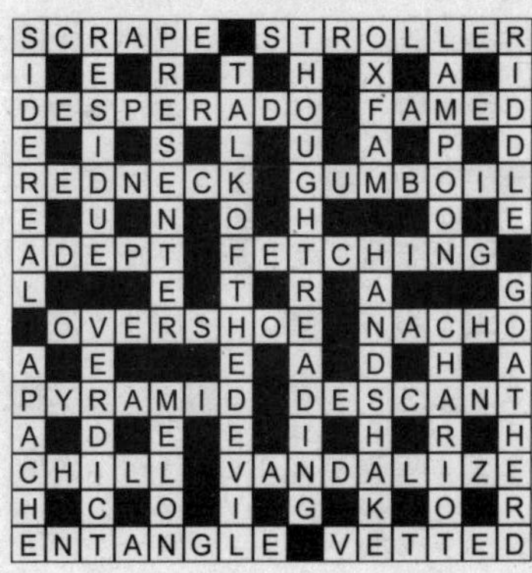

Solutions 94–96

94

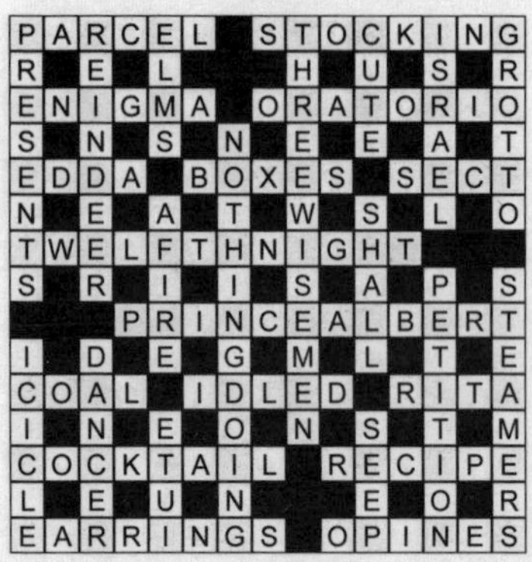

95

96

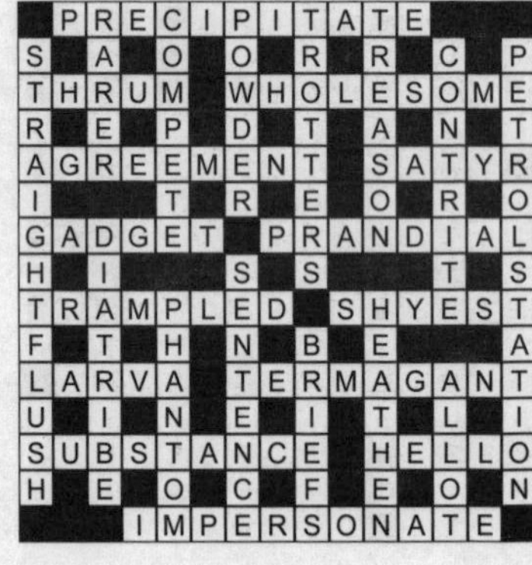

Solutions 97–99

97

98

	C		O		S		K		H		C		B	
P	L	A	N	K	T	O	N		A	T	H	O	M	E
	A		L		U		O		I		A		O	
S	P	R	Y		D	E	C	O	R	A	T	I	V	E
	T				I		K		L		T		I	
B	R	O	N	C	O		E	V	I	L	E	Y	E	D
	A		A				R		N		R			
E	P	I	T	A	P	H		H	E	R	B	A	G	E
			U		O		P				O		A	
C	H	A	R	I	S	M	A		S	E	X	I	S	M
	E		A		T		N		E				L	
B	I	L	L	O	F	F	A	R	E		S	N	I	P
	G		I		R		C		S		E		G	
C	H	A	S	T	E		H	E	A	D	A	C	H	E
	T		T		E		E		W		L		T	

99

Solutions 100

100

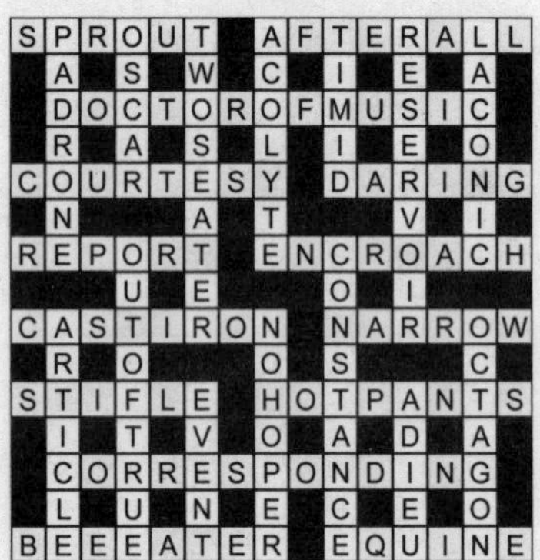

Also available from Hamlyn: